NOT FOR LOVE

VIRGINIA McMANUS

Not For Love

G. P. PUTNAM'S SONS

NEW YORK

© 1960 by Virginia McManus

Library of Congress Catalog Card Number: 60-8474

MANUFACTURED IN THE UNITED STATES OF AMERICA

To Nell
with love

I am deeply grateful for the help of Jack O'Grady and Evelyn Singer, my agent, without whom this book would never have been finished. Her encouragement, advice and friendship were invaluable.

NOT FOR LOVE

Chapter 1

AT NINE THE LIGHTS WENT OUT. The jail dormitory became quiet and the security tank across the hall, where the drug addicts were hallucinating in the dark, built up a chorus of screams. The teen-agers on the sixth floor threw plates and spoons, banking them off the dormitory windows. Across the room a bed bumped whenever its two occupants moved, and their neighbors giggled softly. The mice came out and scampered between the beds. I finally dozed and woke about midnight.

The noise from the tank woke me. Between violent bouts of nausea a woman screamed Spanish prayers; a very young voice shouted hoarse English curses at the guard; someone beat a plate against the bars in steady rhythm. The mice were still running back and forth; several women were snoring. I knelt on the foot of my bed and looked out onto Sixth Avenue. It was raining, the street was brightly lighted and the night clubs were active. The dorm was very cold. Two men in evening clothes fist-fought on the corner. A voice from

15

the sixth floor yelled, "Kick him in the guts!" and a man who had stopped to watch the fight called back, "When do you get out, baby?" A drunk came around the corner, stumbled and fell. I went over to the tiny bookshelf and tried to read the titles: there were several Clara Barton books, a Nancy Drew mystery, *The Red Cross Swimming and Diving Manual.* The books were covered with penciled comments— *In April 12, Out June 22; Doan Read This It* STINKS; *I Never Come Back To This Place.* I took one entitled *The School on the Hill* back to my bed and tried to read in the light of a street lamp. It was written, supposedly, by a twelve-year-old girl in a Vermont convent school. It was about her pretty mama and auntie who came to see her every other Sunday, the pretty school, the lovely sisters and the good wholesome food God had given them. I looked at the frontispiece. It was given to the jail by the Catholic Friends of the Poor. Someone had scrawled *Jesus Help Me* across the dedication. I agreed wholeheartedly.

I returned to looking out the window. An old car with five or six teen-age boys pulled up. One of the boys leaned out and yelled, "Hey Virginia! Are you up there?" I knew he couldn't see me but I was startled. They were about the age my students had been. And for the first time in months I thought about my students, about Chicago, my family . . . and my home.

"By God," Ann said, "I think I see a patch of daylight!" Ann was my roommate, and somehow both of us felt this was going to be our vintage year. Since college we had both made unspectacular records. Ann had spent five years training as a commercial pilot; after graduation she took the only available job, flying a wealthy alcoholic about in his Cessna. He kept the plane in rather shaky repair, insisted on doing some of the flying "once they were out of traffic," chewed tobacco and spit it in a coffee can near her foot.

I hadn't done much better. As an undergraduate at Western State I had worked for a straight A average in Education courses; while other students took the minimum number of hours in the field, I elected every course the school had. In a junior-year "Ed" class I turned out an eighty-five-page thesis entitled "The Ideal School"; it was intended to be to education what Plato's *Republic* was to government. I was so confident that my rebel plan had significance that I typed it on stencils and turned out hundreds of copies; the only public reaction was a disapproving note from the school's office-supplies department asking me if I really needed thirty boxes of paper. Now, several years later, I had made little progress with my teaching. I sat up late at night grading workbooks, supervised study halls, kept order in lunchrooms; on one job I spent two hours a day as a hallway "traffic director." I was as disgusted with my jobs as Ann was with hers. The final blow had come in June when I saw a penciled yearbook comment: Graduation! No more eight o'clocks, no more books, *no more Miss McManus!*

I was heartbroken. I had assumed the children loved me. But this was another year, and things were going to be different. Ann told Mr. Hannibal he could fly his goddam plane *all* the time, she was quitting. She enrolled at the University of Chicago graduate school and was going to be a philosopher.

I had been offered a position as head of the English department at Griffin High School, a large private institution housed in a former Governor's Mansion in the suburbs west of Chicago. Since I had received their letter (describing classes of no more than fifteen students; progressive, creative methods; gifted children), I had driven past the school many times. It was housed in an enormous fiasco of a building, a gleamingly white replica of the White House, with an intricately landscaped campus and an abundance of statuary. The only draw-back seemed to be the distance. I had taught for a while at the Bateman School on the Near North Side and had been spoiled by walking to school each morning. This had been my best experience as a teacher, but I found myself yearning for a more challenging assignment than the quiet, dignified, conservative Bateman School could offer in its cloistered setting of ivy and wrought-iron fences.

Most hopeful of all was our new apartment. Since I had been a child living on the South Side I had wanted to move to an old, Near North brownstone. Ann and I had taken a Near North apartment the year before but it was a fiasco. We had fallen in love with the location. It was next door to the Ambassador East's famed Pump Room. Tall black waiters with plumed headgear ran in and out; the day we applied for the apartment we passed the Eisenhowers going in to lunch; the lake was a block away. It was an English basement with a private entrance, which appealed to Ann; her one impractical wish was to live in a converted cave.

There was little that was English about the apartment but it was very, very basement. And it had many cavelike aspects. The windows opened directly on the alley that separated us from the Ambassador East. We had a twenty-four-hour panorama of the hotel's intimate, and inelegant, workings. We could see the workers toting garbage; we could even smell the garbage if we opened our windows, which we seldom did because of the soot and cinders. Even with the windows closed voices carried perfectly. The cooks and busboys sat on our window sills and smoked, drank beer and sometimes necked with the pantry girls. We could hear their dirty stories and they could hear our conversations. Once, when Ann called from the bathtub for a bar of soap, a kitchen worker called in, "Hey baby? Want me to wash yer back?" After dark, motorcycle cops roared up to the kitchen door for handouts, then sat on their machines, gunning and backfiring the engines, while they ate steak sandwiches. Much later cats fought and mated in the Pump Room garbage.

In addition, it was unearthly hot. The water pipes ran through the living room and kept the temperature a steady ninety-five. In December we were still coming home and taking cold showers. At our New Year's cocktail party the guests finished in their undershirts. We looked for almost anything else and to our surprise found exactly the apartment of our dreams.

We answered a *Tribune* ad for a "Three-room apartment, high ceilings, woodburning fireplace, private sundeck, use of garden and Bar-B-Q pit." The apartment was in a small white house owned by two white-haired men in Bermuda shorts. Don, the older of the pair, had his architect's office on the ground floor; their apartment was on the first and we would have the second floor. They interviewed us on a hot July night in their apartment. It was very dark and lighted with candles; when we sat down on the velvet love seat a cloud of dust rose. Once, when they were out of the room, Ann whispered to me, "This is what I've always imagined the inside of King Tut's tomb would be like." It was no exaggeration. They had three rooms filled—no, packed—with gold, crystal, baroque; with carvings, paintings, tapestries, dark green velvet, purple velvet and undisturbed, feathery dust. They interviewed us formally, asking many personal questions and serving whole pickled black walnuts (shells included) and tea. After an hour or so they began to bring forth their collections—teaspoons, silver teapots, hand-painted China, miniature dogs—and we praised politely and lavishly. They brought out Scotch and large glasses. After several hours they had warmed sufficiently to invite us into their private garden.

The garden was something to behold. Landscaped on three levels, it was surrounded by a high fence. They had imported Japanese flowers, little stunted trees, gnarled shrubs, and many swishy-tailed fish in a deep pond. There was burning incense, tropical birds in tiny gold cages, wandering white pouter pigeons and doves, soft lighting and an Australian guinea pig called Cindy who had no discernible front or back. In a corner pen were nine Japanese spaniels; Japanese music was piped out from the hi-fi. We had been drinking for several hours and I found myself wiping away tears. "I didn't know you missed Japan that much," Ann whispered to me. I thought it was a crude remark; the whole thing was beautiful and rather enchanted. When they asked us to share their home I was overcome.

We moved in on Friday, the fifth of August, with the help of my parents, several colored men and a large truck. My father was rather horrified with the house; by daylight it did appear somewhat gauche, not to mention dusty. The moving men were merely convulsed.

"Dat man," one of them giggled, "say I gotta stop singin'; I'm scarin' dem birds. Bet he got *twenny* them little birds!"

"You see dem squinch-face dogs?" the tall one asked me. "Dey doan look like dogs *I* ever see. Man tell me, doan make noise aroun' 'em, dey *nervous!*"

The short, fat mover kept trying to peek in their apartment as he carried things past. "Dey got," he reported, " 'nuff crap in there ter fill a thousan' junk yards. I seen least ten a dem pink lamps, all alike. You reckon dey sells 'em?"

"It look like a fairy lan', out back," the driver added.

"That it does," my father said, rather sourly.

We had a late supper in their garden, since our kitchen wasn't arranged. I was due at Griffin the next morning at ten and we drank champagne toasts to a successful interview. The evening was cool, the garden genuinely beautiful and we were young. When we went upstairs to our own apartment, we stood on the little sundeck for a while and talked about the future.

Griffin was a long drive from the new apartment. I started

early and before I opened the gates I stood across the street and looked at the school. It seemed dignified, elegant and governmental. I could imagine myself teaching small, intimate classes of students around a fireplace, teaching literature in the English-school tradition. I crossed over.

Jane Andrews, the school principal and bosom friend of Ella Hitchcock, the director-founder, met me at the door. She was a thin woman with blond hair and exquisite green eyes. Miss Jane took both my hands in hers, looked me straight in the eye and said quietly, "Welcome to the Griffin School." I had a flash of I've-lived-this-before that frightened me. It wasn't until much later that I realized why: at my grandfather's funeral, the mortuary director had greeted me in exactly the same fashion.

Miss Jane walked ahead of me, leading the way from the thickly carpeted reception hall to a gigantic office. I was seated in a secretary's office chair and Miss Jane took her place behind an oversized mahogany desk; we observed a moment of silence while she looked me over. During that moment I had a chance to observe both the office and Miss Jane. The office had once been a drawing room: pale blue draperies hung at the windows, shutting out the light; the walls were paneled with squares of ornately carved walnut; long-dead Governors stared impassively from oak frames. Miss Jane was in her late fifties, tired-looking and gentle; a bit of very gray lingerie hung from her black crepe dress. With a fingernail she traced over a pen carving on the desk top as she surveyed me. "Miss McManus," she began softly, "of what faith are you?"

I was caught completely off guard. At a down-state Illinois interview an old board chairman had opened the meeting by asking how much I thought I could live on. Several years before, a Birmingham school principal had started with a question concerning my integration views. (I was not offered the job.) This I had not expected. Something in her childlike eyes told me it wouldn't suffice to say I greatly admired Thomas Paine. "Episcopal," I said finally, but I resented having to say it.

We continued to sit in silence. A branch of oak leaves brushed against the opened window; sunlight filtered through the leaves and made a dancing pattern on the scarred desk top. I watched the remnants of yellow and purple crepe paper that dangled around the room and fluttered with the breeze. Miss Jane was suddenly aware of what I watched. "The children had a carnival," she began, and then made a note on a tiny scrap of paper and thrust it in her pocket. "I'll have the janitors take the decorations down this very day," she explained firmly. "You see, my dear," she returned to the original subject, "sometimes we need a definite faith in God to work with today's young people."

We were interrupted by the sound of voices outside. Then the front door opened, hitting the wall, and slammed; clicking footsteps came down the marble hall. "I'm sorry I'm late," Ella Hitchcock began as she entered the room, not noticing me. "Dear, this is Miss McManus," Jane made a belated introduction. "Miss McManus?" Ella seemed unaware of our appointment. She settled herself in another tiny, upholstered chair. "Miss McManus?" She looked at me for the first time. "Oh yes . . . I know, Jane, you don't have to tell me. Have you discussed everything with her yet?" Miss Jane smiled indulgently. "She hasn't even seen our school yet." "Oh? Well, you'd better show it now. You'll have to help me get those station wagons over to Ted's." We all rose and started the tour.

Four floors of bedrooms, dens, libraries, walk-in closets, pantries and so forth had been converted to school use. I was shown through rooms filled with desk and chair combinations and equipped with blackboards and bulletin boards. In one classroom a tremendous old glass doored corner cupboard filled a corner; many had small bedroom washbasins. We entered a huge bathroom which had obviously once been a butler's pantry. On the walls were a number of penciled four-letter words, comments and jingles. Over the tub was a mural depicting a three-way sex act, and a large drawing of genitals adorned another wall. Jane quickly reached for a doorknob and we left the room. "Oh mercy!" she said to Ella. "Dear, did you have any idea those drawings were there?" "Well of *course* not!" Ella snapped back. "I suppose vandals broke in during the night." Jane wrote on the little scrap of paper in her pocket. "I'll have Pete get those walls washed in a jiffy," she commented as we walked on. I knew enough about schools to understand the fascination obscenity invariably held for a limited number of students in any school, but somehow Ella's refusal to admit what had obviously happened nettled me. It was the first hint of what was to become a most unhappy relationship.

At last we went back to the office. "You have seen our school," Jane began, "and I hope you have seen the spirit of it as Ella and . . ." Her expression froze. A tall, rather handsome, beautifully dressed boy with a blank expression on his face stood in the doorway. He held a radio out to Jane. "Oscar," Jane said firmly, "Miss Ella and I are having a business conference, and . . ." "Radio," Oscar said insistently. "I see the radio, Oscar! Your dear father has bought you a new radio and I think it is splendid! I shall talk to you. . . ." Oscar was not insulted. "Pete . . ." he began slowly, "Pete said . . . I can help . . . him clean." "And you *may help him!*" Jane all but screamed. "Go to help him, Oscar! Go to help him!" On her feet now, she all but shoved him through the door. Jane returned to her place behind the desk and recovered her composure.

"Oscar," she started, "is the son of a fine, respected Christian family. He is perfectly bright but in need of help." Ella broke in with professional confidence. "Why Jane, it's no secret!" She turned to me. "Oscar is from a wealthy family. He will go into a world of society men and women. He is not a regular student here, he attends to learn poise and social adjustment!"

That, apparently, was that. Jane relaxed slightly. The contract was on the desk. "We are not a wealthy institution," Miss Jane said, "but we would want to pay you a fair sum; what would you ask?" I added something to my previous salary and named a figure. Miss Jane and Miss Ella exchanged quick glances, then both nodded. I signed the contract and left. But even as I did I knew that the incident in the bathroom and the encounter with Oscar had hopelessly prejudiced me against the school. But, I reasoned, I had to have a job and it was growing late to make arrangements for next year.

I waited until after dinner to mention the school. Lee and Jan, friends from our college days, had dropped over and stayed for dinner; since the apartment was half-unpacked we were eating on the sundeck. Lee was a successful social worker, Jan was a successful copywriter; they lived efficient, effortless, successful lives in a neat, efficient apartment. I sincerely detested them both. I had deliberately visited them late at night and early on Sunday mornings—and found them bathed, coifed and neatly dressed, sitting in a clean apartment and engaged in useful activities. They had visited me after a week's advance notice and found me partially dressed, sitting in a pile of half-sorted laundry and cursing and weeping with discouragement. They had come over now to tell us about Lee's promotion—she had been made a supervisor—and caught us in a memorable mess; we rushed them out to the sundeck where we sat gazing at the garden and the neighbors' back yards. I was determined not to tell anything about my new job that wasn't efficient, successful and very, very smug.

But I soon found Lee worming a story from me which exaggerated my unfavorable impressions.

When I had told her what she wanted to know and sat rubbing my shins, bruised from Ann's under-the-table kicks, Lee lit a cigarette and settled back. "Well, I don't *know*," she began rather thoughtfully, "but you sure sound like you're off to a good start. The school's got a fine reputation and you make it sound like a home for incorrigibles, and for no good reason. You'd better straighten yourself out or you're heading into trouble. Real trouble!"

Ann tried to change the subject but it wasn't necessary. There was a piercing scream from the yard on our left where a Puerto Rican woman had been leisurely hanging up clothes. "Good God," Jan said, hanging over the rail, "I wonder what's the matter?" Other people wondered too; windows opened in both flanking houses and Spanish faces popped out. The woman continued to scream. "Look, Jan," Lee said. "Look at that funny-looking thing!" We all looked: An ostensibly headless and tailless Cindy was running blind, frantic circles around the neighbor's yard. The clothes were down and the woman ran back and forth over them, dodging Cindy. Puerto Ricans hung from two dozen windows and shouted instructions. A man appeared with a broom and started in pursuit of Cindy. John and Don came out.

"Cindy's over there," Ann called to them. John looked over and saw his beloved Cindy narrowly missing violent blows of the broom. "You stupid sons of bitches," he shouted, "that's my *guinea pig!*" He started toward the yard with Don behind him. "Pig?" "Pig?" the Spanish questioned from the windows. "No pig—some kind of animal!" John dodged the man with the broom and grabbed Cindy; the woman emitted a final shriek and fell in the middle of the clothes. Her husband and son appeared and there was animated talk of calling police, cutting throats, suing for damage to clothes, suing for damage to Australian guinea pigs.

"What *was* that?" Lee asked as we settled back in our chairs. "Well," Ann said, "it's the landlord's pet—" "I don't like to say it," Lee interrupted, "but this is worse than your last apartment."

"Have some more coffee," Ann suggested.

Chapter 2

IN LATE AUGUST I received a very formal note from the Griffin School, welcoming me to the staff and inviting me to a "little get-together" on the 29th. A rose by any other name would merely have denoted the usual long, hot and very, *very* stiff meeting that precedes all school years and is to faculty relationships what a honeymoon is to marriage, without a few of the compensations. Most faculties being quite human, in a matter of weeks the teachers will be visiting each other's homes and going out for after-school beer; some will be feuding bitterly, some will marry and many will sleep together. Knowing this makes the pre-school tea more ludicrous; having to wear fashionable autumn clothes and a hat in August doesn't help.

I wore a too-heavy dark suit and met another woman teacher, similarly attired, mopping her brow on the school steps. I bared my teeth politely and said my name was Virginia McManus; she said her name was Virginia Ford and wasn't it *warm?* (Later in the year she told me the four martinis she had gulped to carry her through the meeting hadn't made her any cooler, and she had been standing there deciding if she should faint.) I agreed that it was *indeed* warm and we went in.

Inside it was very cool and in a singular state of confusion. A number of janitors ran about with what I recognized as Miss Jane's scrappy work orders and much banging of buckets and mops. "Hey, Pete!" one shouted down the stairs. "Dis order I suppose ter do something 'bout the thir' flo hall. What I suppose ter do 'bout it?" "I dunno," Pete answered, peering under a chair. "Go wash it—maybe that right!"

Miss Ella came out to meet us, dragging an anemic-looking young man she introduced as Mr. Rand, the history teacher. Miss Ella was in rather high spirits. "I have a surprise before the meeting begins," she said, herding us up the stairs. "My cousin and his business partner are making a wonderful, wonderful new Home Ec Kitchen for us!" We could hear the pounding and clanking that apparently meant the work was in progress; we could also hear some rhythmic cursing. In a long room at the top of the stairs were two very handsome, mid-fortyish men in unaccustomed work clothes; the one introduced as Clay, her cousin, was waving a crowbar. "How do you do," he said coldly. He turned to Ella. "Might interest you to know," he said softly, "that those fine examples of higher civilization you keep in this place have come here and torn out an entire sink foundation." "Oh Clay," Ella laughed prettily, "don't let these nice people think you're a meanie!" "Ella," Clay continued, "I'm going to put this sink foundation in once more. Then I'm going to sit behind that door until one of your characters comes in. . . ." We stood by awkwardly. "It should be a very nice kitchen," Mr. Rand said politely. Clay pointed the crowbar directly at him. "Why," he inquired gently, "just why do you need a kitchen with all the other equipment

you have now?" Mr. Rand looked terribly embarrassed. Miss
Ella laughed gaily. "What we all need is a nice, hot cup of
tea!" she said lightly. "What we all need," Clay persisted
doggedly, "is a good business where we don't have to . . ."
We were on our way down the hall. Behind us the clanks resumed.

In the library most of the faculty were already assembled
with Miss Jane. When we came in she seated us and rapped
on her desk. "I think we can start this meeting now," she
began, "and first I want to introduce everybody. We'll start
with Mrs. Ford, on my right." Mrs. Ford was sleekly groomed,
in her mid-forties and beautiful. She looked very bored.
"Mrs. Ford has simply decided it's fun to work!" Mrs. Ford
stopped looking bored and looked positively startled. "You
see," Miss Jane went on, "after many years of just being a
happy, happy homemaker, Mrs. Ford has decided to share
her typing and shorthand skills with our young people. And
I think it is just splendid!" Mrs. Ford went back to looking
bored; with a graceful, wedding-ringless hand she traced a
pattern on the desk.

"Mr. Bell, you are next!" A white haired man looked up
from the list he was writing. "Here we have a man who
has given forty-five years of service to young people, teaching
them . . . *mathematics!* And after retiring from the public
schools in June he decided he wanted to go right on, inspir-
ing and spreading knowledge, and he came to us!" Mr. Bell
went back to his list. I could see part of it—he was writing
Order coal on Monday A.M.

A tiny, hunched little bird of a woman was introduced as
Miss Witte, a product of eight years of creative, wonderful-
wonderful service to the Griffin School. While Miss Jane
talked about the service she had rendered, Miss Witte leaned
forward and held her head to one side; I thought she might
be deaf.

"Miss McManus," Miss Jane said, "has come to us after several years of exemplary, creative teaching in some of our country's finest schools. She . . ." I lost interest at that point and I must confess that I spent most of the rest of the time the meeting lasted looking furtively out the window.

The meeting droned on. The older men occupied themselves by watching the twenty-two-year-old Home Ec teacher, a bosomy but rather homely girl; Miss Witte bobbed her head vigorously to indicate she could hear what was being said; several spinsterish-looking women looked hopefully at Mr. Rand. Mr. Rand alternately looked out of the window and at a rather handsome, dark, rumpled young man in a sport shirt and day's beard. I was rather fascinated with him myself; when Miss Jane began his introduction he stopped cleaning his nails with a penknife and listened with some show of amusement. "Mr. Weinstein," she began, "is really a bad, bad boy!" She paused for effect. "You see, Mr. Weinstein took a master's at Harvard—but then he wanted *adventure!* And our Mr. Weinstein, with his wonderful record in philosophy, went into the world to sell . . . Tupper Ware!" Mr. Bell looked up from his list. "Well, actually," Miss Jane amended, "Mr. Weinstein has done a number of other things too. But now our young man is ready to settle down. Not only does he have the academic skills to offer our young people, but also a firsthand knowledge of the world of business." Mr. Weinstein returned to poking at his very dirty fingernails; the introduction went on.

Mr. Rand and I watched a little drama taking place outside. On the steps of a most elegant house across the street sat two rosy-cheeked boys of about fifteen. Every few minutes a car would pull up, the butler would emerge, and the boys would make some comment that empurpled the butler's face and caused the guests to all but sprint up the stairs. There was a five-minute period in which no car pulled up and the boys simply stretched out on the steps and sunned themselves. A dark blue Buick pulled up and the driver helped two elderly ladies out. The boys sat up, the butler came out, and suddenly the pattern changed. The boys raced across the street and the butler chased close behind them. We lost sight of them as they ran up the school porch; the front door slammed, we heard running footsteps on the stairs, a scuffle and loud voices. Shortly after the scuffle Clay, Business Partner, the butler and the boys appeared in the library door.

"Here's one of your little sweethearts!" Clay shoved first one boy and then the other in front of Miss Ella. "Tell her how cute you are! Just you go ahead and tell her!" The confusion was terrific. The boys, the butler insisted, had accused him of being "improperly buttoned" in the presence of some of the finest, yes the very finest people in Chicago. Everyone talked at once. "Stuart," Miss Ella asked the smaller boy, "did you do anything?" It was a purely rhetorical question. Stuart had been alternating shouts of "I didn't do nothing" with "My mother pays my tuition here" all the way from the street. He simply redoubled his protests. The other boy insisted he hadn't done nothing either. Clay threatened to take his crowbar and demolish the new kitchen. Eventually a muttered apology, finished off with a final "I wasn't doing nothing though," was wrung from each boy. The butler walked stiffly back across the street, Clay and Business Partner returned to their task after a few well-chosen comments from Clay, and our meeting resumed. Suddenly Mr. Weinstein spoke up. "You know," he said, "that guy *was* unzipped." Miss Jane jumped. "What?" "That butler," Mr. Weinstein explained, "His pants *were* unzipped." Mr. Bell folded his list and put it in his pocket. "Jesus, Mary and Joseph," he murmured as the next introduction began.

After we had each been honored with some pedagogical clichés Miss Jane felt obliged to refer to the butler incident.

"I'm sure that, as experienced teachers, you all know this sort of thing happens with intelligent, high-spirited young boys." One of the older men whispered something to Mr. Bell and Mr. Bell nodded agreement. I felt certain it had to do with cats-of-nine-tails. "But we also know," Miss Jane went on, "that if we look deeply into any young person we shall know that all is *good*." Miss Ella smiled. "Our young people," she added, "are all products of homes in which there is culture and excellent religious training. We have never had a boy or girl who has gone wrong." It was obvious that Jane leaned heavily on the Lord to guide her in her work. Ella, too, seemed unaware of any problems. And somehow I knew their attitude would inevitably result in making me hypersensitive to such problems as cropped up. For I was a worrier and had always been inclined to magnify my problems far beyond what they actually were.

"Before I assign your classrooms I would like to give you a few little aids," Jane said. "You will need supplies, I suppose, but we shall think of those later. . . . Here"—she produced many little rags from a paper bag—"here are some dusting cloths that may help you." She counted them. "You may each have one." "It looks like," Mr. Weinstein said solemnly, "something heavier would give us more protection." Mr. Bell laughed. Miss Jane hesitated a moment. "Oh, Mr. Weinstein!" she chided. "You are joking with me!"

Miss Jane took me to my classroom. I had seen it before; it was the little room with the corner cupboard in a corner. She gave the cupboard a surprised, how-did-you-get-here look. "Why, mercy!" she said with a genuine start. A small piece of paper and a pencil came from her pocket. "I'll just have Pete do something about this," she murmured, scribbling. I had a vision of a confused Pete washing and waxing it. "There!" she said finally, stuffing the paper away. "Now, you have fifteen desks here. That will be more than enough for the classes you'll be called on to teach. Now is there anything you'd like to know?"

When I left, Jane shook hands with me very formally. As I was unlocking the car door Miss Witte bore down on me. In the bright sunshine her rouge was purple; she waved her pocketbook to get my attention and hurried with mincing steps. "Miss McManus," she began breathlessly, steadying herself by catching my sleeve, "Miss McManus, what room did she give you?" I described it. *"Oh dear,"* she said loudly, confirming my notion that she was deaf. "I had hoped *to have that for mine!"* "I'll be glad to trade with you," I shouted back. "Oh, no-no-no!" Miss Witte laughed mirthlessly. She pulled me down in order to shout directly in my ear. "You couldn't have *my room,"* she stage-whispered, "because it's in *the basement!* They wouldn't put a young lady like you in *the basement!"* I had a fleeting mental picture of basement goings-on; whatever they were I felt certain that Miss Witte was quite safe. As I drove her home I picked up more specific information about the cellar. "You know," she confided loudly, "nowadays, it's boys and girls together, *carrying on!"*

"Ann," I said that evening, while we were packing to go to the cottage, "did you know that nowadays it's boys and girls *together* that carry on?" "What?" I told her about Miss Witte's observations. "Well," Ann said finally, closing a suitcase, "it's the first normal thing you've told me about the place. Maybe there's hope for you yet."

"The cottage" had been a part of my life since I practiced walking by hanging on to the rail and climbing the steps that ran from the lake to the house. All my childhood summers were spent there; in high school we had used it for beer parties; since then it had been my place of escape. That night as we sat in front of a driftwood fire I felt a strange link with all the past summers—with the tiny, vigorous grandmother who had originally owned the house and was long dead, with all the many people who had come and gone there over the years. Ann was rereading *Wind, Sand and Stars* and I had been reading a collection of Browning's poetry. I had just read:

> Your ghost will wander, you lover of trees,
> (If our loves remain)
> In an English lane . . .

I could well imagine the pale soul of Elizabeth Barrett Browning drifting among the ancient trees of England; I could imagine the peaceful, well-organized soul of my grandmother wandering in the formal gardens that surrounded her town house. It seemed logical that Thoreau would settle eternally at Walden Pond if he hadn't turned to city dwelling; Millay would return, I supposed, to the New England coast. I had an unpleasant vision of my soul drifting about looking for Utopia and occasionally resting briefly on a thorn. "Ann," I asked, "where do you suppose your soul will settle?"

Ann looked up from her book, understandably startled. "You mean in what particular section of hell?" "No," I said, "I'm serious." I read the poem to her. "Well," she said finally, "I don't think my soul will stay in any one place—not on earth, anyway. I've often thought when I was flying at night that I'd like to just keep climbing up toward the stars; I guess I'd be more at peace in the atmosphere. Where would yours be?"

I thought it over. "I suppose," I said, "my soul will settle out here in the sand dunes . . . around this house, or by then it would be where this house was." It was true . . . all the memories of people who had been important to me would be centered there. Earlier that summer I had found one of my old drawings in a desk drawer. It was a sketch of my mother. I had been startled to see how blond her hair had been. I had shown it to Mother and she had remembered it as being from the summer of 1940. That evening as I dried dishes in the little makeshift kitchen I recalled an evening fifteen years back when I had experimented with washing dishes in the lake. . . .

Of all the experiences in my life, the cottage alone had never disappointed me. It was the one very certain, very stable factor. After a long winter away from it I would return in the spring and find the house sitting on its hill, scarcely more weatherbeaten than the previous year. No matter how disappointing or chaotic or unstable my affairs of the winter had been, the tall dune grass would be blowing and the sand-cherry bushes would have white blossoms and another family of wrens would have found the little house we had put in the cottonwood for them. Every spring the cottage smelled of damp newspapers and the mice nested in the upholstery. The summers were unfailingly hot and desertlike during the day, the back dunes full of black cherries and concord grapes; nights were cold and full of rain and sudden violent storms. There had never been a fall that didn't color in early September; the bittersweet grew in the same places, the pre-winter storms left strange fish high on the beach, almost at the cottage door. I could never imagine how the cottage would look in winter or that it really existed then, until one Christmas night we drove out and waded through hip-deep snow to spend the evening there. We had built a fire and listened to faint carols on a battery radio.

The cottage was a certainty; I felt sure my soul would try almost every place and finally settle there. We returned to our books and I forgot the conversation until several years later.

It was my last time at the cottage.

A few minutes after my first class at Griffin started Miss Ella brought Stuart Stein in; I recognized him as the shorter rosy-cheeked boy from the butler incident. She waited until he chose a seat, and then looked around the room, skipping over the cupboard that still occupied a corner. "This," she said with an extravagant sweep of one arm, "is what I call a roomful of fine young men and women!" She exited quickly. Stuart didn't waste any time. He sized up his audience, wriggled his nose a bit and announced, "I *smell somethin'* in here." It took a few seconds for the implication to penetrate; when it did the room rocked with loose, gulping laughter. A big, loutish boy in the front row managed to make his chair rock with him. I fixed Stuart with what I hoped was a thoroughly nasty look; he met my gaze with round eyes. "I was just saying," he protested innocently, "that I *smelled* something in here." The few who hadn't caught on the first time understood now. He waited until the laughing died down.

I didn't have many choices. Before I could make a decision he tried again. "I just wonder," he said wickedly, "what it could *be* that I smell?" A skinny boy in the corner twitched wildly and covered his face with his hands when he laughed. I took Stuart by the arm and led him from the room; at the door he stopped suddenly and wriggled free. "I'll bet," he said to his audience, "that if the Russians could get this stink they'd . . ." I rushed him off down the hall to Miss Ella's office.

The office, it developed, was already occupied and I had to wait with a sniveling Stuart while Miss Ella disciplined another student. Then at last the door opened, a chastened youth issued forth and Stuart and I were ushered into Miss Ella's inner sanctum.

"I din't do nothing," Stuart began. He finished with a muttered apology and we went back upstairs. At the door of the room he paused; all eyes were on him. "Well, I'll be!" he said, stepping back with staged surprise. "Somebody's been pretty busy while I was gone!" The laughter began and I felt myself gripped by an unreasoning fury. I knew that in another second I would commit the unpardonable sin of striking a pupil and I struggled to gain control of myself.

"Stuart," I said, "come back in the hall."

We sat down at a hall guard's desk. "Stuart," I said, "what does your mother do when you act like that?" "I dunno," Stuart said, "she laughs, I guess." "That," I said, "is because she is your mother. I'm not your mother. Do you know what I'll do to you if you act that way?" Stuart thought it over. "I dunno," he said, finally. "Well," I said, "I'm not going to tell you what I'll do." We went back in the room.

All through the period Stuart watched me. Twice he started to wriggle his nose and met my gaze; he scratched it instead. By the end of the period he was still trying to work up to another remark. I've bullied him, I thought when the class left. I've intimidated him and I've bullied him. I've spent six years studying psychology so that I can understand and analyze and handle these things in a professional manner. I've done research on human motivation and pathology and I'm a qualified therapist and when it comes to a situation like this what do I do?—I *bully* the child. I didn't feel too bad about it. By God, I thought, I hope I can find the strength to keep it up all year.

At lunch I sat next to Wally Weinstein. When I sat down he made a circle of his thumb and forefinger and said, "Put your forefinger across this."

"Is this some kind of Boy Scout oath I'm taking?"

"Hell no," he said, "just do it."

I cautiously placed my finger across the circle.

"And that," Wally explained, "means that you sit on the boy's toilet."

"*What?*"

"That's what it means," Wally said seriously. "At least

that's what I've heard all morning. Look over there." He pointed to a table where a group of boys were chanting "Dick sits on the girl's toilet" around a delighted, red-haired boy. It went on all through lunch. After the game had been played on everyone it started over, and everybody wanted a second turn.

That afternoon a small window was broken in the hall. The culprit, a nice-looking but rather cross-eyed boy, explained it to Miss Jane when she arrived on the scene. The explanation was plausible enough: A pigeon was nesting outside the window and he and Jerry had of course wanted to catch it. When they couldn't, Jerry told him to put salt on its tail, but they could only find a pepper shaker in the closed dining room. The pepper, when dumped out the window, had been carried back in their faces by the very stiff breeze. They had slammed the window and the middle section had broken from the impact. Miss Jane listened attentively to the story.

"Mark," she said, when he was through, "you have a mother, have you not?"

Mark looked as though he were trying to remember.

"Yeah . . ." he said finally, but with some uncertainty.

"Well," Jane said, "that pigeon is a mother." She let that gem sink in, dismissed Mark and Jerry and dispatched someone to get Pete with a broom. "We shan't have any more trouble with him," she said firmly. "Boys are sensitive, under all the foolishness. It's a matter of reaching them."

Ann and I read their first themes when I got home. I had asked them to write and tell me something about themselves; as an afterthought, and to satisfy a gnawing question in my mind, I suggested they add why they chose Griffin School.

To be blunt, the themes were not very good. Perhaps I expected too much for a first week paper. In fact in light of hindsight I am sure I did. But at the time I was furious at the children and at their inability to organize their thoughts and set them down on paper. And almost inevitably my anger was transformed into a resentment of the school. What I expected I do not know, but I do know that somehow I expected more than I got. Here it was a week after school had opened and already I was nursing a resentment of the school, its students, and its administration. It boded ill for the future.

At ten o'clock Wally Weinstein called. He had found my number in the phone book, he explained cheerfully, and thought maybe he'd drop over. When he left, long after midnight, I knew quite a good deal about Wally and even more about the rest of the staff. He *had* sold Tupper Ware, although without much success. His gimmick was ringing a doorbell and introducing himself as Wally Tupper, son of the founder, out to learn the business from the ground up. He admitted he made few sales but insisted he had access to many bedrooms before the company heard about his system.

Chapter 3

Miss Jane put Wally and me in charge of the first Griffin dance. She suggested that we form a student committee and find out what they would like to do at their dance.

"We don't have to ask them what they want to do," Wally said after she left, "we just have to be there and see they don't do it." "Well," I said, "we might as well go through the motions of a democracy; we could try an all-female committee."

We appointed a chairman, a pretty, long-haired blonde who annoyed me because she chewed gum constantly, but who seemed capable of handling this sort of assignment. She in turn appointed five of her girl friends and we met after school in the library. They had wonderful ideas. One had gone to a college dance where the decorations had included a false ceiling and walls of "angel hair," making the entire gym appear to be in the clouds; she thought we might get a few tons of the stuff and transform the assembly hall. I remembered a brief Christmas experience with one small box of angel hair—it had taken hours of picking with tweezers to pull it out of my hands and some simply had to wear off. The chairman agreed that angel hair was impractical but she had seen a *Life* magazine layout of an "island" party given at a Sigma Delta house; it involved a big pool of water and all the guests had to "walk the gangplank" over it. Many of them had, of course, fallen in the water, but they were wearing almost no clothes so it didn't matter.

Wally gave me a meaningful look. I knew what he meant. I tried to remember what décors I had seen that would be practical. All I could think of was crepe-paper streamers and balloons; obviously such things were not exotic enough. I recalled one spring dance at the sorority house where we had banked a large room with artificial carnations; they were made with pink Kleenex and it had taken days to get enough but it was very luxurious-looking when completed. I described the room and they were enthusiastic—we could, I elaborated, have some of the carnations as centerpieces on tables, and pink candles, and carnations wound around the banisters of the spiral staircase and carnations on the bids.

"Democracy, it's wonderful," Wally said sarcastically when they had gone off to plan dance dresses that would go well with carnations. "It may not be the democratic way," I said, "but it's better than a bunch of excited teen agers pushing each other in a puddle." "O.K.," he agreed. "How do you make carnations?" That was a problem. It had been a number of years. . . . I could remember that you fanfolded double pieces of Kleenex and put a bobby pin in to hold the center and serve as a stem. I went to the drug store for equipment, locked myself in the classroom and experimented. The first attempts were discouraging; after five or six tries a strangely carnationlike flower emerged. I made more. By the time Wally knocked on the door to ask what I was *doing* in there, I had made a couple of dozen. "Not bad," Wally said. He bunched them together and they resembled a very fluffy bridal bouquet. "You see," I said, "we'll put up chicken wire and pull them through." "Not bad," he repeated. I gathered up my flower-making equipment, and went home.

While I was cooking dinner I had an almost overpowering urge to simply stop everything, get out the Kleenex box and begin making flowers. I controlled the impulse but right after I stacked the dishes I took out my workbag, set up a card table in front of the fireplace and started folding flowers. Ann read and I worked; as I completed each flower I would throw it in a shopping bag on the floor. When the bag was almost full, I had been working steadily for over two hours. Ann looked up and said, "You're a damned fool to be doing that." I must have looked hurt for she went on to say that it was nice of me to help the children, but I was already staying until all hours to talk to one of them or sitting up half the night trying to change lesson plans. It seemed to her I could let the janitors do the sweeping and the children do the idiot-work for their own parties; I needed time for my own interests. "But," I protested, "I'm enjoying this!" It was all too true; I hadn't enjoyed anything so much in ages. Once I had figured out the pattern it was simply repetitive, mechanical work; I turned my mind off and let my fingers fly. Ann went back to her book and I filled the shopping bag, went to the kitchen for another and filled that. By bedtime I was very relaxed and foolishly happy.

"What kind of junk is that?" Jerry Prell asked the next day. Wally and I were sitting in my classroom with the committee girls, working on the flowers. "I'm making a carnation," Wally said, and waited for the reaction. Jerry was incredulous. He went out and got some of his friends and brought them back to see a grown man making a flower. "How are you doin' that?" one of them asked. I showed him and he cautiously folded a pink Kleenex; when a recognizable flower emerged he had a hard time looking displeased. "Yer nuts," another of the boys said insultingly. *"Makin' flowers!"* He picked up a Kleenex and folded it the wrong way; Wally straightened it out and soon there was another carnation. "Goddam flower," he said, looking at it. "Hey Jerry, I'll bet you can't make a goddam flower." Jerry had a worse time of it; his hands were the size of hams and less dexterous. It look several demonstrations before he had an acceptable product.

"You know," Wally said to me much later, while we sat over a beer in his apartment, "I've never seen one of those kids sit still before." He thought it over. "What was that kind of therapy you were talking about?"

I hastened to dissuade him from the thought that I was deserving of any special credit for doing what was, after all, my job. But Wally was not the one to be easily dissuaded.

"Incidentally," he said, "how many of those are you going to make?"

"Oh, we'll need *thousands*," I said, trying to appear unembarrassed. I had been turning out flowers from the moment I sat down; I was having a fine time but I was a little sensitive about it. When I left I had another full bag.

That night Ann and I were going out to have dinner with my family. As we were leaving our apartment Ann stopped and looked at the bag I was carrying. "You're not taking those flowers out there are you?" I explained that I was working for a deadline, and I had promised to have hundreds for the next day. "All right," Ann said finally, "if you want to be a sucker I don't care."

It was a strained dinner. As always I had the uncomfortable feeling that two pairs of eyes—my mother's and grandmother's —followed every move I made. Above all, the piercing eyes took in my hair style, my manicure or lack of one, my clothes. After dinner we settled down in the living room and I spread my handiwork out. "*What* are you doing?" Nell, my mother, asked. I explained. The family exchanged glances. Nell went into her bedroom and emerged with pictures cut from fashion magazines; this was a familiar routine and I shuddered. I also speeded up my flower making.

The first picture was clipped from *Glamour;* the model was dressed in an extreme black satin suit and her pale blond hair was in a huge French twist. *"This,"* Nell said, looking at my styleless short hair, "is how you *used* to look." "Just when did I look like that?" "Why," Nell said, "when you were about eighteen—your hair was long like that, and you were beautifully groomed." Nell's memory was not only short, she all but hallucinated. At eighteen I had long hair, that was true. But then she had berated me for wearing it just "yanked back," necessary since I was in training as a swimmer, and for wearing "ugly and unimaginative" clothes. All this was forgotten; she remembered the long hair and imagined the rest. She spread out more pictures. *"Look* at you," she said accusingly. I stopped mid-flower and looked; I did look pretty bad. I was wearing the old tweed suit I'd taught in all day; I had sat in some deliberately planted chewing gum and some of it remained. I was a frump and I knew it. I started the next flower.

More pictures. "If your hair were longer . . ." Nell was saying. I could remember a bad weekend when she had begged me to cut it, shown me pictures of "all the smart people" in short hair, wept and gnashed her teeth; in desperation she had cut her own to show me how pretty short hair was. Now she showed me a series of suit pictures—my skirt was too long, it looked tacky—all the suit pictures had sixteen-inch hemlines.

At eleven we thanked my grandmother for a delicious dinner and left. "I wouldn't go back there," Ann said, poking the starter button viciously, "if those hypocritical, neurotic . . ." It was also a familiar line. Ann contended that Nell was childish and a borderline psychotic; my grandmother, she thought, was a foghorn-voiced, dominating old bitch. My father she felt sorry for. According to Ann my family drove me, insulted me, tried to drag me down to their neurotic level, and so forth.

In many ways Ann was right. It was just that she couldn't understand completely.

That Nell was childish was undeniable. She was also delicately pretty, clever, artistic and very gentle. Nell wore outfits that embarrassed me no end, and she held herself up as a criterion of fashion. She drew actually cruel caricatures of me and of the other members of the family and she was nervous and flighty and nagging, but her intentions were excellent.

Ann could never understand that while we accused Nonnie, my grandmother, of ruining our lives, we were actually very grateful to have a scapegoat on which we could heap blame for all our shortcomings and failures. When we completely flubbed things we could always point to her and say, "You started this whole damned neurotic line." We knew she couldn't really dominate us—we were too stubborn. As a family we were all noisy and outspoken and argumentative and much too frank with each other; at all times there was one nonspeaking feud going on around the house. We were all gossipy and we told both truth and fiction on each other; we had such a sure knowledge of each other's weaknesses and phobias that we could say aptly cruel things, and we had excellent memories to store mistakes and grievances that could be tossed in one crushing heap at each quarrel. We fought until we were breathless and made dramatic leave-takings of each other and always gravitated back together. For better or for worse, and usually more of the latter, we were a family, and whether our bonds were love or neurosis they were very firm.

When I came home from Griffin the next day Ann had dinner cooked. "We're going to eat and get out of here," she said, "before you can start making flowers. I've called Lee and Jan and we're meeting them. I feel," she added, "as though I live in a paper-corsage factory." I refrained from saying "Pardon me for living" and we ate dinner.

Lee was getting along beautifully as a supervisor. One of her directors had told her personally that she was doing such a *beautiful* job, and one of her cases had sent her a handmade bedspread in appreciation. One of the caseworkers she supervised told her she was a person to be emulated. Another case, an old woman, had cried when she left and . . . It was a very long evening.

"Ann," I said as we were driving home, "do you know the Griffin kids have a song—'Hi-ho, hi-ho, it's off to school we go. We learn some junk and then we flunk, hi-ho, hi-ho'— and do you know sometimes I think that's the way they feel about things?" "I'm certain of it," Ann agreed. "Well," I said, "do you think any of them would cry if I left? Do you think anyone there would make me a bedspread, not that I'd want it?" "Just what are you driving at?" Ann asked. "I'm just feeling unwanted," I said. "I work very hard and nobody ever says thank you. Nell says I'm messy and Lee insinuates I'm a flop and to the kids I'm just a fixture, like Pete. I wish I could work with the old bums on skid row or run a home for stray mother cats. I want to hear someone say thank you." "Cats can't say thank you," Ann said. Ann was a very practical person but she wasn't very understanding.

I kept my misery to myself as we drove in silence. I hate my job, I thought. I hate Miss Jane. I hate everybody. I'm not going to do anything for anybody but myself. I wish I could just sit in a little room and make flowers. The thought startled me. I knew I had been enjoying those flowers too much; I had a sudden picture of myself sitting in an institution, my hair grown long enough to suit even Nell, and my fingers working over carnations while my eyes stared off into space.

When we got home Ann was feeling apologetic about her lack of sympathy. "Do you want to work on the flowers? I'll help you," she offered. I shuddered. "No," I said, "the kids are going to finish them, I'm not going to make any more."

I may be ineffectual, I thought, but I'll be damned if I'll go stir crazy.

By this time I had been at Griffin two months and I had become a chronic worrier. I worried if at eight thirty a single one of the eighteen pupils enrolled in my first-period class was not actually there, or arrived from five to ten minutes late. I worried if when I gave tests one boy turned in a blank paper or if more than one or two failed. I woke up at five thirty every morning and lay awake and worried until six thirty. I worried all the time I cooked breakfast and I worried while I ate breakfast and then I had indigestion and hiccuped all morning and I worried about developing an ulcer. We had "Teacher's Guide" books that went along with the textbook series and they caused most of my worries because they stated in no uncertain terms what kinds of reactions good teachers got and what the students were supposed to be accomplishing. For the eight weeks' examination in English literature the book said to ask "searching questions; questions that will force the students to compare the poetry of various centuries in England and to use the intimate facts about the great poets which you have taught them." They gave sample questions and answers; the answers were taken from students' test papers on a nationwide basis. I used the exact questions for my class.

Most of the answers were passable and some were very, very good indeed. But a few were not, including one that went:

The Angel Saxons were big, tall blond men who live on a little islan and wrote poetry that is famus today. One of them was name John Dumm and he wrote all about dying and use to sit in a coffin when he thought.

Another wrote:

> The Jutes and Saxons and Angles were all Englishmen
> and some of them, like Tennyson, were queers and wrote
> poetry to men but not all of them were that way and some
> of the Angles, Saxons and Jutes were women.

In another textbook was an essay on "Laws and Freedom
and *You,*" which the teacher's guide said all sophomores
loved because it made them think, and some of my sopho-
mores hated it and I finally had to read it to all of them because of the few who would not finish it alone. *After your
students have read the essay,* said the Guide, *spend several
periods discussing laws for the ideal society. Have the class
draw up a list of basic laws necessary to insure happiness,
equal rights and good living for all.* After I read the essay to
them I pounded on my desk to wake them up and told them
to write a list of the laws they felt were necessary in every
society.

While they wrote I leaned back and looked out the window at the beautiful campus and red autumn leaves and
little squirrels chasing each other, and I worried. I thought
about ulcers and dying and who would get my books. My
head ached and I felt as though I had a fever; when the class
was over I went down to the infirmary. The nurse wasn't
there so I took my temperature. It was slightly over a hundred. I taught the rest of the day and worried about what
disease I was developing; right after school I went home and
got into bed. I felt very sick and when I read the "Basic
Laws" themes and came to the first of the inevitable few
flunks I felt sicker. It read:

> In a free place people can't kill anybody just the govern-
> ment does that. They haf go to school and keep quiet so they
> can earn mony when they get out. They cant take off theire
> clothes unless theyr married to each other nor can they do
> anything outdoors unless its' in the country or someplace

where their arnt any toilets like in the city. You haf to say
nice things only about people or they can make a judge put
you in jail like almost happen to my father at whre he works.

I read a few more and decided I was too sick to grade
papers. I slept until Ann came home and woke me to ask
what there was for dinner. "I'm too sick to cook," I said.
Ann didn't answer; she turned on television. At eight she
went out in the kitchen and banged around for a while; I
heard her fixing something on a tray and I saw her going
past the bedroom door with the tray. After a few minutes I
called in and asked her where my dinner was. "Oh, I'm
sorry," she said with her mouth full, "I didn't fix you any;
I thought you felt sick." I did feel sick; I was beginning to
feel even sicker. "Do you want anything?" she asked finally.
"No," I said. "I don't want a thing."

When she passed the door with the tray on her way to the
kitchen I asked her what she had fixed. "Oh, just a chop,"
she said, "and some of that salad you made for last night and
the rest of Nell's cake." She went back to the living room and
changed the program. I got up and took my temperature
again; it was a hundred and one. I went into the living room
where Ann was stretched out in front of a fire, drinking
Scotch and watching an Olsen and Johnson comedy. "Would
it interest you to know," I asked, "that my fever is a hundred
and one?" "Oh God," Ann said with quite a show of interest.
"I hope it isn't something I'll catch from you."

I went back to bed. I lay in bed and felt very feverish and
hoped very hard that I had something dangerous and painful
and highly contagious. Sometime after ten the phone rang
and Ann took it in the living room. "It was two of your students," she said, coming into the bedroom. "Harrıson Bass
and Nancy Herman. They said you were sick when you left
school and they wanted to know if you were all right." Ann
sat down and turned on a light. "Because you're sick," she

said generously, "I'll read *Wind in the Willows* to you." I was overwhelmed. I was also slightly suspicious, and asked, "How much have you had to drink?" "Oh, quite a bit," she said. "I was lonely in there with no one to talk to. My mother," she added, "always read *Wind in the Willows* to me when I was sick."

On Tuesday and Thursday nights I went to classes at the University of Chicago's graduate school. Along with several hundred other teachers, principals and supervisors I sat under fluorescent lighting that made us look even more gray and tired than we were, discussing education from the philosophic, scientific and progressive points of view. The next morning we returned to our classrooms and grubbed along with the equipment, space, time and type of students we had, trying not to feel hypocritical. At times the things we discussed were practical; at other times I gave lip service to ideas that appeared to me impossible and even undesirable.

In December the class read a book written by a middle-aged English woman, Miss A., based on her experiences with delinquents. She had taken over a huge and not only long-abandoned but condemned mansion in the most evil of the London slums, gathered a few permissive and dedicated teachers together as a staff, and opened the doors to the hoards of curious adolescents; minutes later she and her little staff were hurled bodily out the door as the children took over the equipment. Standing together on the street—one of the young men was without his britches, Miss A.'s skirt was torn nearly off—they decided they were far from discouraged: They were pleased to find the hoodlums so enthusiastic and spirited. After several more such evenings the children, quite convinced that these good souls were endlessly forgiving, asked Miss A. to take them for a "field trip" to the most exclusive section of the city. After this excursion, during which they had stolen bird baths and lawn furniture from the estates of the rich, insulted passers-by and at one point hoisted Miss A.'s skirts and kept them elevated for a full block, the children were ready to settle down to "organized activity" and requested help in staging a play. The "play" consisted chiefly of improvised and vulgar pantomimes, obscene dancing planned by an older sister who was a prostitute, and a number of unscheduled on-stage fist fights.

The little book ended when, after the children burned the house to the ground, Miss A. was surrounded by them as she stood weeping in the smoking ruins. The children were sorry, they said, for they needed a house and her help. The finale had her roasting potatoes in the ashes of the house and discussing plans for a new building with them while they feasted. Our class felt that Miss A. was sainted and brave and had proved something about permissive methods. I also thought Miss A. was brave and very likely sainted but a damn fool on this earth. The part about the play hit too close to home: Miss Jane expected me to put on a Christmas pageant and I felt a ridiculous fear that it would somehow follow the lines of Miss A.'s production if I weren't careful.

For the previous six years the pageants and plays had been handled by Michael Conner, who taught a variety of classes at Griffin as a substitute teacher when he wasn't directing their plays. For reasons that could only be guessed at, Mr. Conner always chose plays with a part for a large, fat lady and he took that role. The year before, the autumn play was a musical of *Tom Sawyer* and he played Aunt Polly in a gingham dress, white apron and poke bonnet. One of the fathers, who had apparently fortified himself before coming to a grammar-school play, and who obviously didn't know Aunt Polly's true identity, had thrown his arms around Mr. Conner after the curtain fell and wept. "You brought back my childhood and my blessed, dear grandmother," he said. Miss Jane had a difficult time making the children stop talking about it, and this year Stuart Stein had tried to pass a

petition asking Michael to put on *Kismet* and do a belly
dance. To offset this obviously undesirable trend, Michael
was to teach his grade-school class for a while and I was to
devise some sort of Christmas play.

Everybody wanted to be in the Christmas show. What they
wanted to do was make an amateur-hour type of production
and have each clique do a brief skit. The only proposed skit
that involved Christmas was by Jerry Prell, Harrison Bass
and a little fat boy named Gerald Hyman, who wanted to
wear long red underwear, shake cow bells and sing "Jingle
Bells." Other groups wanted to do "Down by the Beautiful
Sea" in old-fashioned bathing suits; one girl wanted to act
out "Take Back Your Mink"; and a number of boys volun-
teered to tell jokes or imitate Elvis Presly. Miss Jane was
heartbroken; she wanted something that would genuinely
reflect Christmas. I complied and turned over class time for
three weeks to casting, practicing and directing a Christmas
pageant of poetry, Negro Christmas spirituals, the reading of
the nativity scene from the Bible and so forth. The making
of invitations to send to the parents drew particular enthusiasm; as always, art work of any kind was fun to them.
We needed a hundred and fifty invitations and they made
them in less time than seemed possible.

The day of the Christmas pageant at least a hundred of
the parents arrived at three o'clock and were seated in the
assembly hall by Miss Jane and Miss Ella, both wearing
corsages of Christmas-tree balls on their old black crepe
dresses. Next to the beautifully groomed and befurred mothers they looked shabbier than ever; I could have wept for
them.

At three fifteen Miss Ella made a welcoming speech and at
three thirty Jane made a very similar talk. And by a quarter
to four it was obvious, to me at least, that for all my work the
pageant was far from a success. Lines were muffed, cues
missed, tempos dragged. On and on it went, with things

getting worse each minute, until I wondered that the audience did not rise as one and storm out of the assembly hall in protest. Instead they actually seemed to be giving every evidence of enjoying their offsprings' collective performance. But I was not fooled for a minute: they were only being polite. And a fierce anger seized me. All the stumblings, the omissions, the lapses were aimed directly at me as part of a subtle yet diabolical plot by the students to embarrass me before their parents and my fellow teachers.

By the time the pageant had ended to a storm of applause I was completely furious and stormed from the building. But a few minutes later I discovered I had inadvertently left my handbag in my classroom and had to return to the scene of my humiliation for it.

Nancy Herman was waiting in my room for me. I didn't say anything. "The kids are waiting for you at Joe King's," she said. King's was the local hangout; I suppose I looked surprised. "They've got Christmas presents for you," she went on.

I suddenly had very mixed emotions. My ego was very bolstered by the invitation to their hangout; my anger suggested that I should send a you-should-be-ashamed message and go straight home. Nancy seemed to look very hangdog. Oh well, I thought, I'll go and roast the remains of my Christmas pageant with them and see what they have to say for themselves. "O.K., Nancy," I said, "wait till I get my coat."

When Nancy and I went in, they were sitting in King's, wearing, according to their fashion, their outer clothes indoors. The boys were hunched in their leather jackets and the girls wore both their heavy coats and their head scarves. They greeted me with what I took to be an uncertainty that indicated they didn't know whether they were to be kissed or killed. I sat down and ordered hot chocolate.

And almost immediately I found how wrong I had been in

my suspicions of their actions in the pageant. They thought they had been wonderful, that the entire production had been a triumph of training over natural inclination.

"We sure weren't going to read poetry and stuff right in front of people at first," one boy said. "Then we decided that if you wanted us to do it, it must be all right. And you know it was a lot of fun."

"But we still figured we'd better do something about it or Miss Ella would have us doing this kind of stuff every week," put in another.

"We planned to all get outside afterwards and yell something but we thought it wouldn't be nice because it's Christmas," the one who was against reading poetry said. I agreed it was nicer not to have rubbed it in. "That poetry was some crappy jazz," Harrison Bass said. "That poem off the Christmas card wasn't as bad as the rest of it," he added.

"What poem off a Christmas card?" I asked. "You know," Harrison said, "the card you said you're sending people." I had forgotten that I had read them the inscription on my Christmas cards; it was a translation from the Middle Ages. "Read that one again," Jerry Prell said, "I was goofin' off and didn't hear all of it." I found one of the cards in my brief case. It read:

Whosoever shall, on this anniversary of the birth of the Lord, go forth with a wisp of hay for a shivering horse; a flacon of red wine for a lost and forsaken crone; a branch of bright holly for the orphan; a bone for a hound lost in the snows; he shall come to the end of his days unafraid, knowing well that he has found Heaven on this earth and shall possess that Heaven through eternity.

"What's a crone?" one boy asked. "An old woman," I said. "My grandmother's real old," another boy said, "and I got to drive her to temple all the time." "I made some guys stop foolin' with a cat one time," Harrison said. "I didn't care nothin' for a cat but those guys were gonna put gasoline on it and make a fire and I told 'em they'd be arrested. My mother's got a cat," he added lamely. I said I thought it was well not to burn cats that way. Several others told of small decencies they had performed. One of the girls said she made up Thanksgiving baskets at Girl Scouts one time; several remembered doing that. There weren't many heroic acts in the crowd but everyone seemed to recall something.

They gave me their presents. I started to say it would have been nice to think of Miss Jane too, and then I remembered the stock answer of my mother's when I gave her anything. "It's nice but I wish you'd given it to your grandmother— she's done so much for you." I thanked them profusely and said nothing about Miss Jane. We all sat around rather aimlessly. I felt they were more ashamed of fluffing their lines than they could admit; also there seemed to be some guilt about their lack of good deeds. "Well," I said finally, "since it's Christmas, what kind of nice things are we going to do for people?" It sounded miserably schoolteacherish but it was obviously what they expected and wanted. It broke the tension. They were all going to do wonderful, kind, fabulous things. We parted in a blaze of good cheer and Christmas spirit and love.

"How did the pageant go?" Ann asked when I got home. I told her exactly how it had gone and how mistaken I had been in my first appraisal of it. I also told her how good and kind they had all decided to be over Christmas. "For God's sake," Ann said, "sometimes the way you carry on I think you don't think anybody loves them at all including you, yourself." Before I could reply, I thought of Miss A. loving them while they humiliated her. I wasn't ready to be that kind of fool yet. But Ann was wrong I told myself. She had to be. I couldn't *dislike* them, my own pupils. And yet I was troubled by doubt.

Chapter 4

IN LATE NOVEMBER OKIE, the oldest of the Japanese spaniels, had developed a deep cough that started at sundown, echoed through the house, worked up to a frenzy of gags and barks at 3 A.M. and continued until I got up. The animals had been indoors since mid-October, and when it was damp the house smelled like a circus tent. To combat this we had sprayed it with an air deodorant—after which the apartment smelled like a pine-scented gas-station toilet—tried to mask it by burning little smudge pots of incense that gave a murky sandalwood, oriental whorehouse atmosphere, and on one desperate afternoon, before Miss Jane came to dinner, we had sprinkled an entire bottle of Arpege around the hall. Eventually we stopped worrying about the odor as our noses became de-sensitized, but the asthma was impossible to adjust to.

"Do you want an aspirin?" Ann asked me, at 4 A.M. while Okie was having a tearing attack. I got up and found some aspirins for us. We could hear John and Don rushing around with the croup kettle and the scent of hot Vicks wafted through the bedroom windows. "I hate to say this," Ann said thoughtfully, "but since that dog is almost fifteen years old, and they have eight others . . ." I agreed. John and Don obviously did not agree and with croup kettles, prayers and antibiotics Okie lived on until the twenty-first of December.

We had put up our Christmas tree that evening and I had to set the alarm at two-hour intervals all night so as to check on the baking of twenty pounds of fruit cake. When the alarm went off at two o'clock I saw Ann, wrapped in a blanket, leaning out the window. "Listen," she said. There were strange voices and strange sirenlike wheezes from downstairs. "The vet's there," Ann explained, shutting the window. "Okie started to wheeze like that at about twelve thirty and the vet just came." I thought about it while I checked the fruit cake. As tired as I was of Okie, I hated to see him die at Christmas.

Before I got back in bed I heard the vet leaving and before I could get back to sleep the commotion from below attested that Okie had died. We got up and went down in our robes to sympathize.

The next morning Don came up to ask us if we could take them, and the remains, over to the crematorium. "I can't stand it," Ann said when he left. "I don't think I can sit in the car with that dead animal." I agreed to drive them alone, but at the last minute Ann relented and got her coat.

It was a sad drive. Okie was, in repose, larger than I had imagined. Wrapped in a blue blanket, his four stiff legs and the gray plume of his tail poking out, he made a dreadful picture. Don and John wept all the way over and Ann drove and I tried to avoid looking at Okie, which was somewhat difficult as his tail was in my lap. We froze in the car while Okie was taken into a most sinister-looking building and maintained silence, broken by sniffles from Don and John, as we drove home in a heavy snowstorm. Back in our apartment I had barely taken off my boots when John, red-eyed and rather dazed, came halfway up the stairs and called for us to come right down.

In the middle of their kitchen was what appeared to be a very small pig with fur, which is apparently the way all Japanese spaniels look at birth. Jill, one of the younger females, was licking it and Don was sitting next to the pair in utter awe. "Where did it come from?" Ann asked, almost as bewildered as John.

"Jill had it," Don whispered. "She had it while we were gone and we didn't know she was pregnant. It's Okie's," he added reverently. There was no comment possible or necessary. They clearly felt it was a miracle, ineffable and irrefutable. We stood in silent respect and escaped as soon as possible.

"Do you think that's really Okie's offspring?" I asked Ann. "I think we'd better not question it in front of them," Ann said. "Anyway," she added, "they don't think it's Okie's either. They think it's dropped down from heaven."

"It's nice having you here," Mother said as we sat around the living room on Christmas Eve. We sat in silence. We were uncomfortable and strained and aware of the clock ticking. "Would you like some cookies?" Nell asked. I said I would love some cookies.

I ate cookies and tried to think pleasant thoughts. "We used to have such wonderful Christmases when you were a child," Nell reminisced. "We were really all *together* then." She waited politely for the implication to sink in. "The cookies are very good," I said. The clock ticked. "Do you suppose," Nell said, "that you'll ever want to live at home again?" I ate another cookie and began to wish I hadn't started on them. "Virginia," Nonnie said, "do you intend to teach school all your life?" "What do you mean?" "Well, you started out so well—you could write and act and now it seems that you're never going to do anything again." "You could get on television, I'm sure," Nell suggested hopefully. "You could teach on television, couldn't you?" "Griffin certainly isn't much of a school," Nonnie added. "Just the other day someone asked me where you taught, and I said Griffin, and they said, 'Do you mean Virginia is teaching at *Griffin?* Why, that's where all the children . . .' "

I watched the snow fall and ate cookies. "It would be nice," Nell was saying, "to have something to brag about again. . . . We used to be so proud of you." "You don't look any too well groomed," Nonnie said. "You used to have your hair long and it was perfectly lovely. The other day someone was looking at a picture of you and they said, 'Does Virginia still have long hair?' and I thought, I'm glad they can't see her with that chopped-off haircut." Nell got a pencil and a piece of paper. "I just want to show you how that looks in the *back,*" she said, sketching away. "I want you to see how it looks where *you* can't see it." "If you let your hair grow you could certainly teach on television," Nonnie said. "Griffin certainly doesn't pay much," Nell said, handing me the finished sketch. "That's the way it looks at the back of your neck and that little sketch is the way it looks on the sides." "You were certainly prettier when your hair was long," Nonnie said. "I suppose Ann thinks it looks nice this way." "If you want to see what Ann's hair looks like," Nell said, beginning another sketch, "I can certainly show you." She finished the sketch and handed it over to Nonnie. Nonnie roared. "That *is* what she looks like! With that long, sharp nose!" "I think I'd better go home," I said; "the snow's getting deep." "You could spend the night," Nell suggested. The clock ticked. "I suppose you don't want to spend the night," she said. "The snow will be deeper by morning," I explained.

Ann had the fire going at home.

"I wonder what Harrison Bass is doing," I said. "I wonder what that poor Nancy is doing." "You know," Ann said, "I don't suppose I'm sympathetic most of the time, but I'm genuinely sorry you feel you're in such a teaching mess." "Oh, I don't think I'm in a mess," I said. "That's why I teach adolescents—they're too young to ever be hopeless. No matter how confused they are there's always a chance you can save them." "What about your own life?" Ann said. "That's hardly happiness—teaching in a rat race." "That's my trouble," I said. "That's why I'll always be poor. All I need is a glimmer of hope and I'll keep working forever. One Christmas Eve in front of my own fire and a handful of snow and a couple of ounces of rum and I think life's worth living. I'm satisfied with so damn little that I'll surely never get much."

Christmas Day, Wally came to dinner and then helped us put up the canopy bed. "Why do you have to swim upstream?" he said. "Why do you have to have an antique canopy bed? Why do you have to have a Victorian bathroom and gild the toilet seat? Why do you have to make enough draperies to cover a city block?" The last remark was aimed at my hobby that had replaced flower making: I had taken up sewing and I carried huge piles of material around with me and sat and stitched while I talked. "I don't know," I said truthfully. "It's as natural for me to make draperies as for a bird to build a nest. I feel I have to *create* my house." "You've practically given birth to this one," Wally said. "When are you going to finish painting?" We had been in the apartment for months and still had ladders and brushes and cans of paint around. "Well," I said, "Ann was *going* to finish it but when we decided to do the bedroom in French antiques she had to stop and refinish furniture."

"You know," Wally said when he left late Christmas night, "as hard as you work you're bound to get someplace." "Unfortunately," I said, "I don't have any place I want to go. I'm completely happy." "Nonsense," Wally said. "You wouldn't be knocking yourself out for a Ph.D. if you didn't have something in mind. I think you've got more ambition than you admit." "If you mean ambition in the sense of 'getting someplace in the world,' " I said, "I lack it completely. I want to know a number of things about adolescents and that's why I'm in a research program, but I don't have any worldly aspirations."

Before Christmas vacation was over, Nell offered to help me refinish the bedroom furniture and I accepted gratefully.

"I hope you have something here for lunch," Nell said before she took off her coat. "The hired help expect lunch." Ann's last words had been, "I suppose the old glutton will eat that steak." "Yes," I said to Nell, "there's some steak left and we'll make sandwiches." "Well, I'm surprised Ann didn't eat it up," Nell said. "I've never seen her leave anything but the plate."

"Oh, Ginny," Nell said, scraping away at the side of the desk, "wouldn't you like to have a baby?" "What made you think of that?" I said. "Well," Nell said, "it seems so foolish to do all this work on a house for nothing." I thought that one over. "You lost me back there," I said.

"You mean you refuse to see the light," Nell said. "Wouldn't you like to have a little, soft, cuddly baby? And make little tiny baby clothes, and teach it to talk?" "As I recall," I said, "Nonnie had to feed me because you said little soft, cuddly babies made you nauseated when they ate." "If you married a rich man," Nell said, "you could have a nurse to feed it and change diapers, and you could have pretty bonnets for it, and I'd make a bassinet and Nonnie would love to make baby clothes." I could see one of Nell's belligerent moods coming up. "I'll fix lunch," I said.

Nell dropped the scraper and followed me to the kitchen. "I don't mind helping you," she said, sitting at the kitchen table. "I know that you're poor and I don't mind helping you. It's just that I know you don't have to be poor. You're beautiful and you could marry a rich man; you wouldn't have to have babies if you didn't want them. You don't have to drive that awful car. You could have a Cadillac. I could have a Cadillac. Nonnie has done so much for you and you could do things for her. You could . . ." "Will you go back and scrape and let me fix lunch?" I said. "I don't know that I will," Nell said. "I don't know that I will work so that Ann can have a refinished desk." "Then go out on the terrace and look at the garden," I said.

"Go out and look at the garden," Nell said bitterly. "Go out and look at somebody else's garden. You love flowers. You could have a garden. You could have a swimming pool. You could have a mink coat. That isn't much steak."

"There's more in the refrigerator," I said. "How much do you want?" "Well," Nell said, "I suppose that's enough, but I'm certainly not interested in saving any for Ann. Do you have any tomatoes?"

"All that beauty going to waste," Nell said, cutting her steak. "The other night when you left I watched you getting into the car and I thought, What a waste. If I were young like that, and beautiful, I wouldn't be teaching in any old school and driving an awful old car like that." We chewed away on our steaks for a moment and Nell continued to look very sad. "You had so much promise as a child," she said wistfully. "I had so many hopes for you."

"Have I disappointed you completely?" I asked her as she was leaving. "No, of course not," Nell said. "In many ways you're sweet and kind and honest. I had just hoped for so much more, and I'm still hoping."

Chapter 5

NEW YEAR'S EVE Ann and I stopped at Nell's for a drink before going out. "You look lovely," Nell said. "I think slacks are nice for New Year's Eve." "We're only going to play cards with Wally Weinstein," I apologized. "Oh well, I think crap games are lovely for New Year's. It would be lovely to wear old slacks and shoot craps with someone I admitted never took a bath." I was horrified. "I never said Wally didn't take a bath." "You did so," my grandmother joined in, "you said he never shaved."

"Slacks wouldn't be too bad if you had long hair," Nell said. She brought a stack of clippings from the desk. "This girl"— she indicated a model from *Playboy* with undisputably long hair and velvet slacks—"looks nice in slacks because her hair is long." "It doesn't hurt that she has a forty-inch bust," Ann commented. "This picture," Nell said, "shows how most women your age dress for New Year's Eve." The picture showed a group of models in full regalia and chinchilla coats. "It would be nice if I could tell people where you went on

New Year's Eve, instead of having to lie and make up stories and then cover up afterward," Nell said. "It would be nice if you had a boy friend and if you went to an actual party on New Year's and if you went to the Pump Room sometimes. It would be nice of you . . ."

"We'd better go," Ann interrupted. "We're late." "It would be nice," Nell finished, "if you had somewhere to go on New Year's and didn't have to drive to your mother's for a drink and could go someplace like the Pump Room to drink." "You asked me to come over," I said. "Well of *course* I wanted you to come," Nell explained. "If you have nothing better to do on New Year's Eve I'm happy to serve you a drink. I just think it would be nice if you . . ."

"I'm going," Ann said. "I'd better go," I said; "we're late." "You'd better hurry," my grandmother said. "You might miss the first act of the crap game."

The school seemed full of strange faces the day classes resumed after Christmas vacation, although actually there could not have been more than eight or ten new students in the entire high school. "What can we do with all of them?" I said, for even ten new enrollments so disorganized things the first day that I felt it was impossible to start classes. The halls seemed filled with slouching new boys and girls. The first-period class was a total loss. The new students wandered in and out to see what was going on; the regular students were out looking at the new ones; and Miss Jane ran through my classroom twice, both times tossing vague apologies "for disturbing your class" over her shoulder. After a half hour had passed and it seemed that at least fifteen new boys had stood in the doorway and looked me up and down (actually no more than two or three could actually have appeared), I went up to Wally's office and said, "Are we supposed to be having classes or just what's going on?"

Mrs. Ford, who was already comfortably seated with a cup

of coffee and a cigarette, said, "Have some coffee and relax."
In a few minutes we had several more teachers and we all sat
and waited.

"Wondered where everybody was," Mr. Bell said, coming
in and easing himself into a chair. "There seemed to be a lot
of confusion in class. We do seem to have some fine new
young men and women," he added. We sat and drank our
coffee until after the bell for second period rang and then
Miss Jane came in and said, "I am so sorry for the confusion,
can you people come to my office?"

In her office she explained that in a private school like
Griffin where new students were only admitted between
terms, there would have to be a few days' confusion while
they were oriented and assigned to classes. "If you would
simply attempt to carry on classes as usual, being flexible, of
course," she said, "we can get things organized very quickly."

I am certain that everything Jane said was true, and that
this was but a passing disruption. But the fact was also undeniable that confusion was the one thing I was not
equipped to face at the moment. All the doubts and mis-
givings I had had about myself as a teacher, about my students, about the school at the beginning of the school year—
which had gradually faded away until they had surged up
again when I had been so mistaken about the pageant—all
these would, I feared, come flooding back to overwhelm me
if I was faced with the strain of having to get used to new
faces and with having to establish a new routine and ward
off the inevitable confusion that would exist until it took
hold.

All morning I went through the motions in a daze, sitting
dejectedly at my desk during the third period when I had
no class. Even when Nancy and Harrison brought me coffee
from Wally's office between the third and fourth periods as
they often did, I could not engage in the usual light banter

that I normally indulged in with them, and they crept out crestfallen after only a minute or so of heavy silence.

At lunch the dining room was an inferno and Mrs. Ford, Wally and I ate in his office with the door closed. While we were eating our peaches the door burst open and an unfamiliar boy's face looked around the corner and disappeared, leaving the door open. "I think we are in for an unpleasant term," Wally said, getting up to close the door.

The afternoon was a torment. It seemed as if every time I started on something new there was another interruption. Actually I doubt that there were more than a half dozen interruptions all told, but in the frame of mind in which I was, it seemed as if there were scores of them.

The second day Ella, Jane and Wally brought the new students into the classrooms one by one and, although it was difficult to teach with the several new additions, at least the introductions were finally over and finished. By the end of the day I had about twenty in each class, which meant the room was filled to capacity and one of the new boys had to use an extra swivel chair which was borrowed temporarily from Wally's office. I pushed my desk back to a corner and shoved my file cabinet into the hall.

Then the new boy who had been given the swivel chair from Wally's office discovered that he could lean back in it and spin. He pulled up his knees and made one complete revolution and then gave me an insolent look and spun it around twice and looked at me again. "Get up," I said, working my way between the chairs to where he sat, or rather, spun. I took the chair and by much pushing and shoving got it out into the hall. "Where th' hell am I gonna sit?" he said. That was a problem. Jerry was sitting near the door and I said "Jerry, go up to Mr. Weinstein's office with him and bring down a straight chair," and then I worked my way back to my little space at the front.

A few minutes later Jane appeared with Jerry and he said,

"There *are* no more straight chairs," and pushed the swivel chair into the room. She left and the boy, whose name turned out to be Howie Berger, sat down and spun. I worked my way to the back, opened the door and shoved both swivel chair and Howie Berger into the hall and slammed the door. The bell rang before the incident could go further.

The next morning it was snowing heavily and after I parked my car in the alley I got my feet completely soaked cutting a path to the back door. Up in my room I took off my wet shoes and stockings, pulled on my red-and-purple slipper socks which had been a Christmas present from Phyllis, accepted my morning coffee from Harrison, lighted a cigarette and settled down at my desk. "Get a load of her," a strange boy in the doorway said to an unseen companion, and then there were two gawky boys looking at me. "You come to school in them shoes?" "Of course," I said and went back to my paper. Inwardly I boiled. We had had the usual minor disciplinary problems before, I thought angrily, but we'd never had this sort of rudeness. When first period began I was still angry and thinking of better retorts than I had made and I wasn't in a mood to find all the new boys with piles of clay on their desks.

"Where did you get that?" I asked one of them. He looked away and the others laughed. "Where did you get it?" I repeated. "Swiped it outa the art room," one of the others answered for him. I knew that Mr. Cranshaw kept a barrel of clay for the grade school but I assumed that those doors were always locked. "You'll have to take it out of here and wipe the desks," I said. No one moved. A very dark-skinned boy with a shoulder-jerking tic took a handful and began rolling it into a ball. "Come with me," I said, and I took him and a big glob of clay down to Jane and said, "Miss Jane, the new boys have stolen huge piles of clay from Mr. Cranshaw and I cannot have it in my classroom." Jane looked up and I realized with a start that she looked ten years older than she had the summer before. "Miss McManus," she said wearily, "there has been an accident in the kindergarten and I'm trying to contact a mother on the telephone, and Ella is very sick at home and I must call the doctor for her. Please try to handle the matter yourself, even let them keep the clay and we'll think about it later."

The next morning the library was flooded. Miss Witte went to get books before first period and when she opened the library door she found that the huge room was quite literally well over six inches deep in water. Pete and Wally and Sam Rand waded through and turned off the water and then got buckets and mops and started the cleanup.

First period was a total loss because everybody had to watch the mopping and pretend to help, and when the water was gone no one could go to class because of soaking-wet shoes. The boys ran up and down the halls, waving their shoes to dry them. Someone put Vicky's shoes in the dumbwaiter on the second floor and sent them down to the kitchen, and when Jane went to the kitchen to retrieve them some of the boys ran up to the fourth floor and rang for the dumbwaiter and got the shoes up there. The morning went without classes ever starting and after lunch, classes were all but empty.

"So many of them had wet shoes," Jane said, when Mrs. Ford came down to tell her there was no one in class. "I suppose they might have become sick."

Chapter 6

"DON'T YOU EVER MEET any interesting men?" Nell asked me. "And I don't mean Wally Weinstein," she added. "Where would I meet any?" I asked her. "I see Mr. Bell and Mr. Rand, and Wally, and Mr. Cranshaw . . . and Clay and Pete, and the landlords. Whom do you think I'd find interesting?" "When I was your age," Nell said, "I found interesting men. What about the fathers?" "Well, what about the *mothers?*" I said. "Do you honestly think I could go out with married men who are fathers of my students to boot?" "I didn't mean that," Nell said primly. "They could be widowed, or divorced, or even separated and it would be all right." "Not if you could see them," I replied. "We have the saddest bunch of fathers I've ever seen—they're all blustering, cigar-smoking, *successful* men." "Success isn't the worst thing in the world," Nell said, "and I'll bet they're not *all* like that."

"Actually," I said, "they aren't. You remember Sid Jeffers, the boy I told you about who chugalugged almost a fifth of whisky at the prom and it turned out that he'd filled the bottle with punch? Well, his father is just as much a four-flusher but he's ungodly handsome." "Does he have a wife?" Nell said eagerly. "He has had about four, I think," I said, "and he has one now, and he's looking for more." "Well, does he ever *look* at you?" Nell asked. "Yes," I said, "he even looks at Miss Jane. At the last P.T.A. meeting she had a low-cut dress and he almost lost his balance trying to peer down her bosom."

At that meeting Holt Jeffers had gone from Mrs. Ford, in whose ear he had whispered during the business session, over to Jane, and finally he made it over to where I was sitting, stitching away on my draperies. "You look domestic," he said, and added, "and very sleepwithable." When he leaned over to whisper the last part I was all but knocked over with a gust of alcoholic fumes, but I wasn't particularly shocked. Since the beginning of the year he had established himself as a "ladies' man" and while his new wife sat and talked to other mothers he played knee-and-ankle games under the tea tables with various women including Ella Hitchcock, complimented and flattered with open insincerity and was inclined to pinch any female under eighty. He was the head of a very successful firm of architects and he had invited me to business luncheons, on sneak cocktail dates, trips to Arkansas on his expense account and, on many occasions, to bed. I refused all his invitations and it didn't dampen his spirits in the least; he proffered outrageous invitations to everyone with such a humorous touch that he was never taken seriously.

At this meeting he was without his wife, very much fortified with liquor and very purposeful. "Your husband," he whispered with another gust of whisky, "wouldn't mind if I just took you for a cocktail." Before I realized the implication I said, "Oh, I don't *have* a husband." "You don't?" he said. "I always thought you were called Mrs. McManus." "I am," I said. "All of them call me Mrs. McManus, but that's because they assume all adult females are married. They call Jane 'Mrs.' too and they know she isn't married." "Well, I'll be damned," he said joyfully. "Why, I'll be a dirty son of a bitch! Where do you want to go for a drink?" "I can't go," I said. "Look," he said, "I didn't really mean to scare you off, but my wife's out of town, almost, and I'm very lonely and if we could just have one drink I'd promise to go right home to my wife." "I'm really sorry," I had said, and I gathered up my yards of drapery and left.

"See?" I said to Nell. "He's the only good-looking man around and who would have him?" "I would," Nell said frankly.

The next Friday night we had a P.T.A. meeting to plan the Spring Carnival and Holt came in slightly late, slightly drunk, very handsome and conspicuously without wife. "My wife's really in California this time," he said, sitting next to me. "That isn't why I wouldn't go out with you before," I said. "I'm no moralist; there was just no reason to go." "Don't you *like* me?" he said. "Of course I like you," I replied, "but I'm busy, and I have a home, and . . ." "Tell me over a cocktail," he said. "Just go out with me for a few minutes."

During the meeting I thought it over, and it occurred to me that it would make Nell profoundly happy if I went on a casual date once in a while, that Ann was at her mother's and I'd be going home to an empty apartment, and that after a P.T.A. meeting I needed a drink. I almost shocked him to death by going immediately after the meeting to get my coat and saying "Let's have that drink." "You'll go with me?" he said in genuine surprise. "Yes," I said, "I think it's time someone called your bluff."

We went to the Top of the Rock and sat looking out over Chicago and he told me about himself.

He insisted his only success had come because he was a fool. Fresh out of college he had been invited to join a major firm, and one of the partners asked him to his suburban home for a weekend to talk the deal over. In the middle of the night he had tried to pour a drink of water in the dark and, not being able to find the hidden light switches, tipped over what he thought was a carafe, mopped it up with some kind of cloth, groped his way to the bathroom by feeling along the wall, drunk from the faucet and felt his way back to bed. When the sun came up he had discovered the "carafe" had been an Italian inkpot and he had covered the white rug, mopped ink up with the brocaded bed spread, made inked handprints over the brocaded wallpaper going to and from the bathroom and finally left inked footprints all over the carpet, sheets, and a slipper chair. He repacked his weekend bag and ran like hell.

For a week he sat at home, let the telephone ring, drank and wept and cursed. Finally he gathered his courage and drove to the estate to apologize and clear the incident. The maid let him in, explained that the gentleman of the house was in conference with some other gentlemen and left him in a reception room, where he paced the floor, and finally sat on a little settee that made an odd noise when he sat down. Getting up quickly he discovered he had sat upon the pet chihuahua that was napping under the cushion, broken its spine and squished it fatally. Again he made a run from the house, and this time he packed all his things and kept running until he came to Chicago, where he found a job with his present firm which specialized in educational construction, a fact which caused him to know many prominent figures in the college world.

The story had a profound effect on me. For once I had found a person who had made a *faux pas* that topped my most prominent ones, and he had obviously become a disgustingly successful person. I began to actually like the man.

"Has anyone," Holt asked after the fourth drink, "ever told you that you are perfectly beautiful?" I pushed his hand off my knee and moved my chair a little—he had an expert habit of pulling a chair with his foot until I was all but in his lap.

"You are just lovely," he said after the fifth drink. "You are really a beautiful, beautiful woman." Any illusions I had had about him were worn off. With great diplomacy and effort I maneuvered him out to the car and home. "You are lovely," he said when he stopped in front of the house. At the door I fished his hand out of my blouse, shook it in what I hoped was a cordial manner and escaped.

"Persistent little son of a bitch, isn't he?" Ann commented at 3 A.M. when the third batch of red roses arrived. We put them in the bathtub with the others and went back to sleep until five when the first of the telegrams came. YOU ARE A LOVELY, LOVELY WOMAN, it read, AND I WANT TO TAKE YOU TO THE RIVIERA. "I thought it was Arkansas," Ann said. "That was before he got drunk," I said.

"Oh, Ginny," Nell said when she read the telegram that evening. "I think that's *very* flattering. I want to keep this. There's someone I'd like to show it to." "You can't show that to anyone," I said; "he's got his name on it and he's a student's father and he's married." "Oh, that doesn't make any difference," Nell said, "he could be a widower, couldn't he? When are you going out with him again?" "He could be a widower but he isn't," I explained, "and he's awful and I'm not going out with him again." "Well," Nell said, "that's very noble but I would like to be able to tell people you were going out and you don't have to do anything immoral with him. Couldn't you just date him?" "I'm not being noble," I said. "I can't stand him." "I get so discouraged sometimes," Nell said.

When I came home I found Ann arranging pink roses in the living room. She had tacked a note on the front door that read:

> Roses are red
> Violets are blue
> I think somebody wants
> To shack up with you.

"I don't think," Ann said, clipping stems, "that I'd encourage him any more. John and Don have roses all over their house and this is the last vase."

At ten o'clock he called and Ann told him I wasn't home and at eleven he called and at twelve I talked to him. He was fairly sober and he asked me to a big education association dinner for that Sunday night. I accepted. "I think you did the right thing," Ann said. "It puts it more on a business basis and if you want to teach at a college next year, it might help." Nell was overjoyed but for different reasons. "You don't want to teach *all* your life," she said, "and he can't be as bad as all that." "I'm just going for business reasons," I said. "I don't like him and he's married." "I told people he's divorced," Nell said, "and if anyone asks you, you went to the Pump Room that night." "If who asks me?" "Anyone," Nell said. "I've told lots of people."

At the dinner we sat at a corner table with six college presidents. Holt had been with them at an education convention in Atlantic City and they were reminiscing. The high spot of the trip had apparently been a plaster-of-Paris replica of manure that was planted on lobby floors, on chairs, in beds and as a centerpiece at a banquet. "Did they do anything other than play with that toy?" I asked Holt on the way home. "Well," he said, "I finally had to hide the damn thing so they could get some work done. I told them they could have their pile of crap back after they got some resolutions passed."

"Who cares what they did on their convention?" Nell said when I told her. "Did he ask you out again?" "Yes," I said, "he asked me out again. He asked me to go with him to the Trustees Association meeting at a college. I'm supposed to talk to the president about being Dean of Women there next year." "Maybe you'll be married and won't have to be an old-maid dean," Nell said hopefully. "I should think," she added, "it wouldn't hurt if you let your hair grow out. I imagine *he'd* like it better that way." "He's married," I said. "I don't like him and he's married and I *want* to be Dean of Women." "I can only pray," Nell said piously. "For his wife to die?" Ann asked. "We'd better go home," I said, "it's starting to snow again."

On Saturday afternoon I took a pair of gold lamé pajamas and a hostess gown with what appeared to be ostrich feathers back to Saks Fifth and collected the hundred and eighty dollars. "What would I *do* with that kind of stuff?" I asked Nell when she moaned over returning the things. "Maybe you won't always *have* to live in a tenement apartment and teach in a second-rate school," Nell said. "Maybe you could strain yourself and get in a situation where you could wear gold lamé pajamas." "I'm just as glad she took them back," my grandmother said. "I'd hate to see Ann wearing them." *"Ann* wearing them?" Nell said. "Can you imagine that hawk-nosed thing in gold lamé pajamas?" "Are you going out with him again?" Nonnie asked. "I don't know," I said. "Well, you may say he's a mess," Nell said, "but he's certainly better than Wally Weinstein. I'd rather go out with a man that took me places and gave me lovely gifts than spend New Year's Eve with someone that I admitted never took a bath."

After several trips to Saks Fifth I developed a phobia about walking in with what my family had always called "hotel underwear." "If these gifts keep up," I told Ann, "I'm going to suggest he send me the money instead and save me a trip." "It wouldn't be a bad idea," she said, trying on a black chiffon something-or-other before I returned it. "If he weren't such a fourflusher you could tell him that you need a bit of fur and maybe you could return a few minks." "I'm not really going into the business," I protested.

When I accepted the first gift from Holt I also accepted the fact that he wasn't doing it for his health. Holt was not a subtle man but I wasn't resentful, I just delayed the inevitable as long as possible.

And it soon became a cat-and-mouse game, with Holt trying to maneuver me into seductive situations. Once he made
elaborate arrangements for us to eat alone in a hotel suite
while everyone else went miles away for dinner. He announced his plan at the last minute and explained he had to
wait at the hotel for a long-distance call, and to my vast relief
another man said he'd wait too because he didn't feel like
going out in the snow.

Less than a week later I went to meet Holt at his office and
found him rather drunk from a long lunch conference and
completely alone. "Where's your secretary?" I asked immediately. "Told her to go on home," he said. It was Friday afternoon, a hazard I'd forgotten. "Well," I said briskly, "we have
to meet people at the Sherman so we'd better get started."
Holt went to the closet and took out his coat and briefcase
and then changed his mind and put them back and went over
to the couch. "Come on over here for a minute," he said, and
patted the cushion next to him. I had a flash of absolute
panic. I'll just leave, I thought. There's nothing keeping me
here and I can just leave. I glanced at Holt and he looked
rather amused. "Oh, for God's sake," he said, "come on over
here." I felt incredibly foolish. I'm twenty-four years old, I
thought, and I've let this man keep me and now I'm acting
like Little Eva. But I can't go through with this. At the same
time I remembered the story of the man who asked his wife,
"Are you certain you want to go through with this?" as she
was being wheeled into the delivery room. I walked very
quickly and with a bravado I didn't feel and sat on the edge
of the couch.

"You've got the most beautiful legs I've ever seen," Holt
said. He ran his hand over my stockings. I said "Thank you"
because I didn't know what else to say; I felt jittery and
acutely uncomfortable. He pulled me down and I took a
deep breath before he kissed me and tried to force my mind
to think of other things. I'll get home by eight, I thought, and

I can make a fire and . . . It usually worked but this time the absolute discomfort of being energetically slobbered on was too distracting. I tried to pull away. "For heaven's sake, Holt," I said as he rolled on top of me. I tried again to push him away and straighten up. "We've got to be at the Sherman in fifteen minutes," I said. "We'll make it," Holt said. He kissed me again and I felt a surge of claustrophobia from being under two hundred pounds and in the tangle of my suit and blouse which had pulled out. My furs were being crushed under me and I groped for them and pulled them out and threw them on the floor. "I love you," Holt said. "I really do. I love you." I was terrified and crushed and furious and I had an overwhelming urge to say a brief, explicit four-letter word, but my suit jacket and blouse and slip had all somehow pulled up and were around my neck and I felt choked. "I love you," Holt said. "Your tie is in my face," I said weakly.

Later in the bathroom I tried to straighten out my clothes. I wet a paper towel and scrubbed the heel marks off my stockings and pinned my skirt where the button was missing. "Hurry up, honey," Holt called in. "We're only five minutes late." "I *am* hurrying," I called back. I tried to take the lipstick off my neck with cold cream. My back and the back of my neck were stiff. "Do you have any mouthwash here?" I asked through the door. "In the little cabinet," Holt said. I gargled loudly and hoped he would think it rude. Apparently he didn't for when I came out he said, "You look beautiful." "For God's sake," I said, "I look as though I've been sleeping in the park." "You look," Holt said, "the way a beautiful, passionate woman should always look." I caught a glimpse of myself in the mirror at the elevator. I looked strangely pinched and tired. Passionate, I thought. My back was very stiff. I wonder if when a woman wriggles because she's being squashed flat a man thinks it's passion.

The night before Holt and I went to the Trustees' convention I stopped to see Nell. "You look so pretty," she said. "I haven't seen you look like that in years. If you'd let your hair grow," she added, "you'd be beautiful. I suppose you still think he's so awful. I think he's being very nice to you." "I doubt if he's doing it to earn Boy Scout points," I said. "You don't always have to suspect motives," Nell said. "Many, many men have done lovely things for women and not expected anything in return." Before I left she brought out some *Vogue* clippings. "Just in case you should go shopping while you're gone," she said, "here are a few ideas." "I think he's getting enough ideas without any help," I said. "Oh, don't be vulgar," Nell said. "Just keep it on a *high plane*."

The next day was Friday. "Where are you going after school?" Vicki asked me when I took off my coat, and my guilt feelings lurched to the surface. Did half the school know about Holt? Had his half-witted son found out and told everyone about it? "Why?" I asked Vicki. "Because you aren't wearing your old-lady shoes," she said logically. I looked down in surprise. I had fallen into the habit of wearing rather sturdy shoes around Griffin because I ran up and down stairs so much, and now I was wearing very pointed pumps with very high heels. It hadn't occurred to me that anyone noticed how I dressed. I guess Nell's right, I thought. I have been slipping, but it hasn't been my fault. When you work fourteen hours a day and you're poor as a church mouse you can't be expected to look nice.

"Why is your hair done?" Phyllis asked me when she came in. "It's Friday and you aren't wearing black," she added. "Do I always wear black on Fridays?" I asked her. "Yes," she said, "you always do." My *God,* I thought, I'd have died if I'd known these kids were watching me like that. While I dusted the room, one of the myriad disgusting jobs that went along with teaching, I tried to think of why I wore black on Fridays. The kids must think I'm in secret mourning, I thought. But I guess I just am so limp by Friday I wear something that won't show the dirt.

By afternoon I realized why "old-lady shoes" were a necessity. I ran down the stairs for the fifteenth time, in this case to tell Jane that someone had turned on a fire extinguisher and the fluid was running all over Mr. Bell's room, and the secretary said, "Good heavens, I don't know why you refuse to use the elevator!" I boiled with suppressed rage. I didn't use the elevator because all the mechanically and criminally inclined boys in school played with the mechanism. Once they had trapped the poor helpless little librarian in it by fixing it so the doors wouldn't open and it simply went up and down and then they made a fire in the grease pit at the bottom of the shaft, possibly to scare her and more likely in the hope of roasting the woman. The secretary was one of those eternal optimists who felt far above such things, putting her trust in God and her common sense in storage. I got Jane, who was also afraid of the elevator, and together we climbed up all the stairs and with Pete we mopped up the fluid.

By three fifteen I gratefully put on my coat, drove my car around to Maple Avenue where Holt was waiting in the Lincoln and handed him my suitcase. "Had a rough day?" he said as we pulled away from the curb. "As usual," I said. "Are all Lincolns this delightful?"

The weather was clear and bright and the highway was free of traffic and as we picked up speed I relaxed. To hell with Griffin, I thought. To hell with bills and income tax coming up and trying to figure things out. I haven't gone any place farther than the bathroom since I left college and I might as well enjoy this. "Want to stop for a couple of cocktails?" Holt said as it was getting dark. "I do," I said. We stopped at a roadhouse and had two drinks each and I felt perfectly wonderful.

But even through the glow of the cocktails I found my

mind turning to problems. It was dark when we started back on the road and, as always when it's first dark in the evening, I felt a terrible, empty loneliness. Why *am* I going on this trip? I thought. If I do become a dean down here I can't finish my work at the University. I'd have to teach two years and then take a year off and go back and how could I *ever* save enough in two years to support myself a whole year? It was the eternal problem in teaching. The beginning salaries were pathetic and the only way to work up to a livable wage was to do years of graduate work and that was expensive and took time that a teacher never had, especially if the teacher tried to do extra paid work to support herself and pay the university fees. It was an endless and an almost impossible cycle.

If I went into the business world as Holt did I wouldn't have to worry, I thought. But I don't want anything but teaching. If it just paid enough to live on I'd gladly work twelve hours a day in order to teach in the right way. But I can't put in those hours and do graduate work and run a reading clinic to pay my rent and take students for therapy in the evening to buy clothes so Nell won't be miserable. There just aren't enough hours in the day. There weren't. I never had enough sleep and still I had to do things at odd hours. I washed dishes at 2 A.M. and got up at four to grade papers before school and did the ironing at ten when I came back from evening classes. I talked to myself while I drove back and forth to school because I was too confused to think things out. I would go along muttering things about grocery lists and picking up the laundry and calling a parent and sending the money to Edison before the lights went off. I made lists to assist my memory and lost the lists. And I despaired that I would ever get anywhere.

At seven we arrived in the town and went directly to the house of a university official where the meeting was being held. While we were drinking cocktails the executive of a nearby college came in with his wife. "My *heavens* what a drive," the wife said as Holt helped her out of her coat. "We started late and Charlie had to just speed to make it." "We sure did," Charlie said. "We got going so fast when we passed Danville that we hit a cat and knocked it fifty feet. Mary hates cats," he added. "Thinks they're sneaky. Any time one crosses the road she wants me to hit it." I looked at Mary in a new light. She was a rather pretty, plump, gray-haired woman in a dowdy dress and an equally dowdy, Sunday-go-to-meetin' hat. I wish I could think of something nasty to do to her, I thought. Something *really* nasty.

We had dinner and then went back to the living room and listened to a number of "brief talks" that were very long. I was very bored. I found a little note pad in my purse and I tried to make a few budget calculations. My last pay check had slipped away and Jane had promised they could advance me something but this was no solution for it would only mean there'd be that much less when the next check came. I made a list of the parents who owed me Reading Clinic and therapy payments—several owed me for weeks back, usually the same parents who owed the school for months of tuition. When these parents came to meetings in their Cadillacs I felt very resentful. Nell's birthday was the next week, and Ann's was in a month and I had a three-hundred-dollar tuition bill at the University and a two months' charge bill due at Marshall Field's. I had a two-hundred-dollar dental bill and the car would either have four new tires and some major surgery or a trip to the junk yard and I'd have to get a new one. I stopped the notations. It simply can't be done, I thought, not on my salary. I work an extra four hours a day and with that I *might* be able to live, not decently but at least stay out of bankruptcy, if the parents paid their bills but they don't. Summer was coming and that meant a salary cut; summer-school salaries were three-fourths and sometimes only half of the regular figure. Most of my reading-clinic and psychological-therapy cases would be going away for July and August. I tore up the budget list. To hell with it, I thought. Writing it down just makes it worse.

At ten Holt said, "Let's get out of here for a few minutes," and we slipped out a side door and went to the car and lighted cigarettes. "I don't know how the hell to ask you this," Holt began and then stopped. *Not* in the car, I thought. He *couldn't* want to do it in the car. He took a couple of drags on his cigarette and said, "I guess I sound like a goddam pimp, but this is what happens at all our conventions—I've got a bunch of guys that want to be fixed up with girls, and . . ." I was so vastly relieved that he didn't want to romance in the car that I wasn't particularly shocked. "You know," he went on rather lamely, "if you wanted to do it the way other girls do . . . well, you'd make a hundred for any of the guys you saw—I'd pay you if they were my guests and otherwise, like if you saw Charlie Maxwell, he'd pay you." He put out his cigarette and we sat in silence.

Charlie Maxwell. "Does Charlie Maxwell want to . . . go to bed with me?" I asked. "He does," Holt said. "He can't stay at a business meeting ten minutes without wanting to dump his wife and get a girl." I thought about the dowdy, puffy little wife who liked to kill cats. "I don't blame him for wanting to get away from her," I said aloud. "Who?" Holt said. "Charlie?" "Yes," I said. "I'm not surprised he'd want to get away from that little porpoise who hates cats." But sleeping with him was another thing. A hundred dollars. Not a gift or plane tickets or even a mink stole—no pretense of this-is-for-friendship or maybe-we'll-get-married. Just a straight business deal. No trips to Saks Fifth to get refunds. It was what I had secretly wished the relationship with Holt could be—no pseudo courtship, no long hours of attentive listening and pretending to be in love and getting the money in a roundabout way. It was the honest way to conduct such affairs, but now that it was offered it frightened me—I had no idea it could sound so cold. "I don't know if I could *do* it," I said to Holt. He didn't answer. I thought about bills and overdue notices and how much I disliked Charlie Maxwell's wife. "But I'll try," I said. I wish I could invite his push-faced little wife to watch, I thought. I was shocked at my own vulgarity. But the idea *was* funny.

At midnight Holt drove me over to the town's best hotel and I went to Room 1719 where Charlie Maxwell was waiting. I knocked at the door and he opened it in his underwear and black socks and garters and shoes. He was drunk and his underwear was very droopy. "We gotta do this fast," he said, "because Mary'll be havin' a fit." He took his undershorts off and threw them over a chair and climbed into bed. He's getting into bed with his shoes on, I thought, my surprise at this being greater than my reaction to seeing a man nude from the waist down for the first time. The old slob is actually getting into bed with his shoes on. "Come on, honey," he said. "Mary'll be havin' a fit."

I took off my clothes and got into bed. I wonder what I'm supposed to do, I thought. It wasn't necessary to do a thing. In less than three minutes I was alone in bed, and Charlie Maxwell was in the bathroom, splashing water with the sound effects of an elephant at a watering hole and calling over the snorts and splashes. "That's th' hell of gettin' old," he hollered cheerfully. "When you're a young pup you can keep humpin' all night, but when you're old you're just like a jack rabbit!"

I lay in bed listening to his vigorous washing and thought, And this is sex with a man. This is what is supposed to be the motivating factor in life. This is what ten million dirty jokes are written about and why people get married and what people are supposed to spend half their lives thinking about and trying to get. This is the force behind Antony and Cleopatra and Romeo and Juliet and a thousand couples on park benches. Charlie came in, drying with a towel and looking positively elated. "Feel like a new man," he said, pulling on his shirt. And this is what men pay a hundred dollars for, I thought as I got up and went in the bathroom.

Sunday night as we drove back to Chicago I pretended to be asleep. Holt was driving fast and the motion of the car was lulling; I kept my eyes closed and thought about the weekend. I've made five hundred dollars, I thought. I don't have to sit on pins and needles worrying how to stretch my Griffin check. That was a relief—to be able to teach without the nagging thought: I'm doing this for less than I'd make if I'd never gone to college—I'm doing this for less than any parent of any of these kids makes and I've been in college for seven years so I can be this poor. I thought about Holt's Lincoln and about my car which had an interesting wheel shimmy that made every drive remind me of the summer I earned my fall tuition by driving stock cars on a dirt track. I can't see why I can't have a Lincoln, I thought. Or at least something that doesn't play "Nearer My God to Thee" on the horn every time I go over twenty.

It didn't amaze me that I had been able to go to bed with five men, all complete strangers, without guilt or horror or even as much revulsion as I had anticipated. I hadn't enjoyed it—I hadn't expected to enjoy it. I had simply used the most expedient means of getting the money that I had to have. And when I left the bed after being with the second man, a college business representative, I had thought, When I drove stock cars to pay for my sophomore year, no one could see why I did it. It was dangerous and filthy and I still have scars from glass slivers, but I knew it wouldn't kill me and I was poor and I had to do something that was drastic enough to pay well. That got me partly through college and this will get me through my doctorate and it's nobody's business but my own.

Holt interrupted my thoughts by saying, "Do you want a drink? There's a good place up ahead."

"I imagine this was one hell of a dull weekend for you," Holt said over our daquiris. "Would it make it up to you if I took you to Haiti next week when I go?" "It would," I said. "I've never been to Haiti." I could have added, "I haven't been any place. And at the rate I had been going it would have been another ten years before I could have gone to Miami." To Holt, going to Haiti was just another side-line business trip. To me it was going into another world. And I was ready for another world—the one I'd lived in for twenty-four years had worn me down.

In a weekend I had changed, technically, and become a whore. Inwardly I hadn't changed a bit. There had been no trauma, there were no feelings of guilt. There was no remorse. Sex just wasn't that important to me. There was no salary in the world large enough to induce me to teach something I didn't believe in; there was no price at which I would have sold out my opinions and beliefs and convictions. The world to me was what it had always been, a world of Mind. And Mind to me was Truth and Beauty and God and I'd never worried much about the physical; sex was part of the temporal as much as eating and sleeping—something that had to be done to survive on this planet but not exactly the reason for being here. I thought Charlie Maxwell had the right idea. He could pay a hundred dollars and spend three minutes and go back to his life and the more permanent business of being a college executive for another month and keep his mind where it belonged.

Once when I had asked Jerry Prell what he was thinking about, the poor lout had answered with commendable candor, "What I'm always thinkin' about." I had thought at the time, I wish he could do it and get it over with and then maybe I could teach him English. There was something rather disconcerting about trying to teach *In Memoriam* to a group of fifteen minds that were all dreaming The Great

American Dream of long legs and Maidenform bras. And I knew it was a dream that was going to keep them busy until they got married or found some other way to resolve it. It was as an old German professor I once had for psychology had told his classes, "If you need a drink of water or have to go to the bathroom for God's sake don't be polite—leave the room and take care of it. If a person's thirsty he can't listen to Bach or read Shakespeare, all he can do is think about water. It isn't that water's more important than Bach. It's just that unless a person's physical needs are fulfilled he can't do any of the important things." He had also added, "And that's probably why the human race hasn't gone farther than it has. When a man could have been writing something immortal he was most likely thinking about lunch or where the toilet was."

Aside from Ann and my family, Wally was the only person who knew about my relationship with Holt, and he thought it was hilarious. One morning I found a poem of Thomas Hardy's he had typed up and left on my desk; it was "The Ruined Maid" and he had marked certain parts with a red pencil:

"O, 'Melia, my dear, this does everything crown!
Who would have supposed I should meet you in Town?
And whence such fair garments, such prosperi-ty?"—
"O didn't you know I'd been ruined?" said she.

—"You left us in tatters, without shoes or socks,
Tired of digging potatoes, and spudding up docks;
And now you've gay bracelets and bright feathers
        three!"—
"Yes: that's how we dress when we're ruined," said she.

—"You used to call home life a hag-ridden dream,
And you'd sigh, and you'd sock; but at present you seem
To know not of megrims or melancho-ly!"—
"True. One's pretty lively when ruined," said she.

—"I wish *I* had feathers, a fine sweeping gown,
And a delicate face, and could strut about Town!"—
"My dear—a raw country girl, such as you be,
Cannot quite expect that. You ain't ruined," said she.

"Don't take offense, 'Melia," he had added. "I'm just tired of eating pork and beans and I'm trying to find someone to ruin me."

With spring and warm weather things seemed to have become unbearable at Griffin. Where cold had driven the students into the building and Wally had driven them into classes, they now stayed far away in the park or on the street. At lunch the dining room would be crowded and in the first class after lunch the rooms would be almost empty as they trooped back outside with hats and balls and blankets. I was furious and I went down and said, "Miss Jane, if you'll give me jurisdiction I'll see that once they're in this building they stay until the last class."

"How would you do it?" she asked fearfully. "I'd lock the doors," I said. "I'd lock the doors downstairs and I'd lock every classroom door and I'd keep them in the building."

Jane removed her glasses and turned them over and over and said, "My dear, I can understand your feelings. But you are so wrong. You cannot force a child to remain in a school building at noon time in the spring. And it is better to have them come back a bit late than to take the kind of measures you advocate or try to punish them in other ways. Once the novelty of spring wears off, they'll return on time, but your way would only encourage obstinacy and retaliation which would plague us for weeks to come."

"I don't know," I said. "I know you are concerned, and I am concerned, but I just don't know. . . ." I saw defeat and I was too furious to admit it to Jane. "You are concerned about tuitions," I accused her, knowing even as I did it that I was wrong and that I was ending my career at Griffin as surely as if I quit on the spot. "You're afraid if the children are punished, you'll lose students, and it isn't true. There isn't a parent here who wouldn't appreciate it if someone took over if their child needed punishment." Before Jane could answer I got up and left.

Later in the day Jane stopped me in the hall and said, "I don't want you to think I'm angry about what you said. You are a person of deep understanding and I hope you'll try to understand me, and my position." "I understand you and I know what you are going through and in many ways I admire you," I said. "But I can't approve of your way of running a school."

At my first meeting at the school I had heard about their beautiful graduation, but I'd forgotten all about it. Then one day Wally said, "By the way, I'm supposed to pass the word that song practice for graduation begins tomorrow morning before classes." "Graduation?" I said dumbly, and abruptly realized that the school year was almost over, and miraculously I had survived. But I did not think I could hang on through another year.

At eight fifteen the next morning we herded everyone we could catch into the assembly hall and Jane passed out song sheets for "Halls of Ivy"; Wally caught my eye and winked.

The singing began and behind me a boy blew his nose with amazing force. Soon the whole row behind me was involved in nose blowing with the loudest, nastiest sound effects imaginable. From across the room there were similar blasts followed by loud snuffles and indescribable sniffling. "They aren't really blowing their noses," Phyllis said. "They just hold the Kleenex up and make noises with their tongues." She demonstrated a razzberrylike noise. "See?" she said. I saw.

Between the nose blowing and the laughing the singing was completely broken up. "I think she's seen about enough,"

Wally said as we went down the hall. "Let's talk to her at lunch."

"But perhaps they *had* to blow their noses," Jane said. "Maybe they had colds. It's spring." "That's not the point," Wally said. "We're adults and we're being made fools of." "Oh, Wally," Jane said, "they're not making a fool of you. They love you."

"I'd as soon talk to the students," I said cattily when we were outside.

Chapter 7

Two weeks before graduation I gave up completely. I felt that I had tried everything, had failed at everything and time had run out so that there was nothing for me to do but throw in the towel. I think the end for me came when I accompanied a busload of fifty down the outer drive to the Goodman Theater. All the way one small group threw paper and leaned far out the window, trying to catch onto passing cars and chanting "Cheer, Cheer, The driver's full of beer." In the theater I had sat boiling inwardly. When one student, sitting a few rows in front of me, put his feet up and an old lady said, "Keep your feet off my hat," and he replied, "Keep your hat off my feet," I knew I should have intervened and punished the miscreant but at the thought I had shuddered in misery and pretended to the scandalized woman next to me that I didn't know where such children came from. Back at the school I accepted the general critique that *Tobacco Road* was a stuffy play, the theater manager was a fairy and they were going to tell their mothers the school had pro-

vided a defective bus because the poor old vehicle nearly
flew apart under their blitz.

Realizing desperately that I had to get hold of myself and
reestablish my authority, I had suggested to the sophomore
class that we stop reading modern plays, since it caused them
such great pain, and write our own play. They voted this
down as worthless because after it was written it would just
be thrown away, and who wanted to write for no *reason?* I
countered by saying that we would put on the play for the
whole school and was promptly informed that such theater
was on its way out, *nobody* went to see the old-fashioned
kind of theater, people went to movies. Movies were so
much the vogue, I was further informed, that four members
of the class had their own movie cameras.

"Well," I had said, throwing caution and common sense
to the winds, "why don't we write a screen play and film it?"
and as a result we had, the next day, four movie cameras,
twenty-five actors, and props, courtesy of a student who
owned his own horse, consisting of a saddle, several pairs of
manure-caked boots, lassos, spurs, long lines and so forth.
With such props only a cowboy film was possible and they
still felt it old-fashioned to write a play first; they simply
wanted to take the cameras to the park and *act.* The sample
movies I was shown consisted of much running uphill with
incredible speed and leaps, a trick I was told involved revers-
ing the direction of the film, fist fights artfully directed with
much upstaging and use of the old one-two, and a couple of
on-the-grass love scenes. These had been made after school
several weeks before and at different times, but put together
they formed an excellent take-off on an old Jean Cocteau picture. Despite my commendable resolution, I could not face
the thought of such a film and so the idea had to be aban-
doned entirely and we went back, with tears and curses, to
Wilder's *Our Town,* left over from the days of the legitimate
stage.

I had tried reading aloud to them as a means of force-feeding the material that had to be covered, and my voice was scarcely audible over the scuffling of feet, cracking of knuckles, writhing and moaning. I found only one story that seemed to suit them—the tale of the boy who cut out his mother's heart and, on the way to deliver it to his wicked lover, tripped, fell on it and heard the heart say "Have you hurt yourself, my son?" They insisted on embellishments concerning the actual cutting into the mother's chest, the type of instrument used to saw with, the appearance of the heart, the amount of blood involved and the exact shade. They demanded so many exact details that I almost feared they were asking for a blueprint in order to go home and try it.

Following a University of Chicago education-course suggestion for personalizing the curriculum and "starting where the children *are,*" I had them make lists of the subjects they would enjoy reading and writing about, or discussing and using as a base for research. I found they were interested in death; sex; mutilation; the macabre; monsters; sex; people dying in accidents, wars, duels, plagues, and by methods of torture; sex; cowboys and Indians, but only in pulp form; football; girls who become nurses (one vote); how to breed quarter horses (one vote); what can happen to you if you play with yourself (one anonymous vote); and sex. After reading the lists and compiling them I continued reading Thurber aloud since it was unanimously detested and no one could cry favoritism.

To enforce discipline I had tried calling offenders in after school for little chats in front of an open fire in the library during which we drank Cokes and toasted marshmallows, and I tried to create a permissive atmosphere in which they could freely tell me why they refused to come to classes, didn't own a notebook or a pencil, didn't care if they flunked everything and liked to sit in the dank, odiferous basement all day. I tried selecting certain ones about whom I felt slightly hopeful and showered them with Tender Loving Care, stopping them after every class to praise and pat and encourage them, writing eulogies of praise on any messy little paper they cared to turn in, writing little sticky notes of praise to their surprised mothers (who no doubt thought it was sarcasm) after any slight improvement, and going along with *their* interests, which involved me in currying a horse and seeing two horror pictures after school. I drew the line when I was invited to a beer party in one student's basement, to be held while his parents were in Bermuda.

When these measures failed I tried a more negative approach, and in little private conferences I suggested that their behavior might lead to futures in manual labor, penitentiaries and hell. I was told that their fathers' businesses would keep them from labor, their fathers' political connections and/or their own craft would save them from jail and nobody believed in hell any more. On a few desperate occasions I forgot myself and shouted and screamed at them, with such excellent results that it frightened me when I realized that intimidation was much more effective than reasoning.

During the two weeks prior to graduation the weather was simply beautiful, sunny and warm, and everyone could hardly wait to get out of school each day. As I would leave the front door each afternoon, I would see the students' cars double-parked in front of school, the convertible tops down, and everybody running back and forth arranging groups to go to the beach and out to the forest preserves. The ones who didn't have cars either sat in Joe King's or one of the other Maple Street hamburger places or went a scant two blocks from the school to a small park. As I drove past Maple Street and the park on my way from school they hailed me cheerfully and I gritted my teeth hard and waved back.

As I sat in my classroom day after day, the problem of final grades plagued me. Following the English tradition the school had a three-day Final Examination period during which the schedule was changed to permit three-hour exams. I couldn't imagine what I could devise that would take three hours, and I felt certain that my teaching had been so inadequate that almost everyone would inevitably fail. I wondered what would happen to those slated to graduate. The school would have no graduating class and it would all be my fault.

I finally made up long objective exams and stayed up till 3 A.M. typing and mimeographing them. The freshman exam was last and by that time the utter futility had overcome me.

I was wrong. Whether it was because I was a better teacher than I thought or the students had followed a system of going "eeny, meeny, miney, mo" on quizzes or through caprice, almost every student passed.

At four o'clock on the afternoon of the last final exam there was to be the Final Graduation Practice and only three students had failed and would not graduate. But the rehearsal was a shambles for in the aftermath of exams student spirits were far too high to permit an effective rehearsal of anything. Since all the teachers were involved in the ceremony we were gathered for the practice, and we politely sat in the assembly hall until five when Miss Jane asked us if we would each take the names of six graduates, call their families and inform them that there would be another Final Graduation Practice on the following day, which was the day before graduation.

At four the next day the entire graduating class turned out and plowed through the mechanics of the ceremony.

"I'd like to see you and Wally for a moment more," she said to me as the faculty left. "I know what you are thinking," she said, "but I want you to stay with us through summer school. I can promise you that in the fall some of the things you want will be accomplished and I'm certain you'll feel completely different about the school."

The graduation was, as Jane had told me a year before, perfectly beautiful. It was held in one of the big lakeside Chicago hotels. The room was filled with flowers and at the back, in the area set up for the tea, there was a fountain that flowed pink punch and tables of elaborately iced and decorated little cakes and sandwiches and one enormous cake that was in the shape of a mortarboard and inscribed *Griffin High School—Scholarship, Service, Loyalty*. The parents of the graduates were dressed to the teeth and the graduates were glowing; the boys wore new suits and waved keys to new cars that had been "surprise" graduation gifts and the girls wore multiple petticoats and bouffant dresses and corsages. "I'm so proud of Bobby," one mother said to me when we shook hands. She had tears in her eyes and her husband was patting Bob on his shoulder and smiling fatuously at him. "We've waited so many years to see our boy graduate," she said, clutching at his sleeve.

The graduates walked in double file, a girl and a boy together, and the girls carried a dozen roses each and walked under an arc of roses held up by as many juniors as could be forced to come, and there was a Presbyterian minister who spoke on "Using Our Educations to Build a Tomorrow." We ate little cakes and talked to the beaming, nervous parents, and the graduates went off in bunches. Everything should have been wonderful, but then one little group of students maliciously informed me they were headed for the movie at the local theater where they intended to put Spanish fly in the Coke machine in the hope of causing a bacchanal. The trouble was that, as so often before, I took their nonsense seriously.

"I'm through for a week," I said when I got home. "For one week I don't have to worry about other people's problems." "What would you like to do?" Ann said. "Do you want to go away for a week?" "I guess I can't," I said. "I like to think I'm free but Holt said to stay on tap in the next couple of days."

The next night at seven thirty Holt called and said, "We're entertaining some businessmen who want to build a big new plant and I'll pick you up at eight." I was in the middle of cooking dinner and I turned down the burners and said, "Ann, you'll have to finish this yourself," and turned on my bath water and started getting dressed.

For these occasions I was simply introduced as Karen Winters, and Holt would explain that I was a teacher and then leave me with whomever I was to entertain for the evening. This evening when he picked me up Holt said, "There's a guy from an aircraft company who's being wined and dined tonight, and for God's sake if he asks say you're a Republican, and let him do all the talking; he's an egomaniac and he'll talk an arm and leg off you; and wipe off some of that lipstick and start out acting like a real prude and let him think he's teaching you something you didn't know."

"Anything else?" I asked. "Come to think of it," Holt said, "there is. We've got two other girls who'll be there and we're putting them on the two assistants this guy's got with him, just to keep them out of the way, and we've said they're secretaries from the President's office at Lincoln College, and if he asks you, say you don't know them." "How did you get secretaries from that school?" I asked. "They're two girls we keep on the payroll," he answered.

The dinner was at the Pump Room and I called Nell just before dessert and said, "I'm at the Pump Room and I'll be out late but I'll talk to you in the morning." "Oh, honey," she said, "are you having a good time, and who are you with?" "I'm having a very dull time," I said, "and I'm with the president of a West Coast aircraft company." "Well," Nell said, "you may think it's dull now, but later on you won't regret it. After all, you're only young once, and it's better to have memories of being *in* the Pump Room than of living in the garbage heap behind it, and anyway you're making us very proud."

Back at the table the president of the aircraft company stood up to let me back in and when I sat down he said, "Were you calling your boy friend?" "No," I said. "Did you suppose that a schoolteacher would have a boy friend?" He took it quite seriously and said, "Well, I guess you don't meet many Clark Gables around a high school. When I was in high school I gave a couple of my teachers a break—I wasn't such a bad-looking guy when I was young." "When you were *young?*" I said. "Why, what do you think you are *now?*" From across the table Holt caught my eye and winked.

Sometime after midnight my executive said, "Look, I know we'd have to be very careful, but do you think we could sneak out of here and go upstairs to my suite for a few minutes?" "Oh, *dear,*" I said, "I don't know *how.*" "I know," he said. "You excuse yourself to go to the powder room, and then I'll say I have to make a long-distance call."

No more than fifteen minutes later, as we were on our way down in the elevator, he whispered to me, "I'll bet when you came along on a dull old evening like this you never dreamed this would happen." "I certainly *didn't,*" I said. "I'm over-whelmed."

"Holt," I said as we were driving home, "how did that man get to be president of *anything?*" "I dunno," Holt said. "Maybe he sat on somebody's pet dog. That's a good way to get ahead." "I'm serious," I said. "This business is about as subtle as the con games at a country carnival." "I guess you're right," Holt said. "That other damn girl slipped and said she slept till noon every day and wouldn't get up sooner if the building were afire and no one noticed it. I guess people believe what they want to believe. That aircraft guy wanted to believe you fell in love with him at first sight."

"Did this really help business that much?" I asked. "Maybe it didn't help but if we didn't do it we'd be through," Holt said. "Once something gets to be standard practice in business one group can't just *not* do it. It's like taking them out for drinks while you talk business. It doesn't set them on fire to get a free drink, but if you *didn't* take them out you'd be on the Cheap Sonofabitch list."

The girls that Holt used on conventions and at meetings were usually secretaries who worked for the organization, girls who were kept by one of the executives or, in the case of a little redhead, the wife of a junior executive. None was a professional—that is, full-time or admitted—prostitute. When a major car company sent representatives, the large meeting that ensued required several more girls and Milly and Bobby were imported. They were the first "real" prostitutes I had known and I was frankly quite interested in them. Bobby was a slightly masculine girl with large dark eyes and a Southern accent; Milly was a *Vogue* fashion-plate type who affected elegant manners. From what I gathered in the scuttlebutt, Bobby came only to see that Milly didn't forget and enjoy her work, but Milly talked incessantly about her "gentleman friend" who "worked out of a bank." "Just how does one work out of a bank?" I asked Holt. "If it's the guy that waits outside for her," Holt said, "I'd guess he robs them." I had seen glimpses of him and he was as slick a gigolo as any B-movie gambler. He didn't look like the bankers I had known.

The last night of the meeting we were still drinking champagne at 3 A.M. and Milly finally called me into the washroom and said, "Sal's waiting outside and I gotta leave because he has to be at the bank at nine." "I'll explain that you had to get home," I said. When I want back in the living room Bobby cornered me and said, "Did she go out to meet that sonofabitch?" "If you mean Sal, she went because he had to be at the bank early," I said. "I wish that slimy little Dago would get caught," Bobby said bitterly. Since most bankers didn't "get caught" I thought it reasonable to ask her what she meant. "Pushing dope," she said. "He thinks he's so damn smart, keeping it in a safety box at the bank, but I've known other guys to work outa banks like that and they got caught."

After that when I "double-dated" with Milly and she grandly discussed Sal's banking interests, I felt that I understood the situation. I agreed with Bobby that he would soon be caught—it didn't seem logical that a bank would overlook such an enterprise for long—and I felt sorry for Milly, who seemed so proud of him. And when the bank did take notice and Sal was arrested by a combined group of FBI men, local police and treasury agents, I asked Milly, who was in widow's weeds, to come over to the house for a drink. "I don't think I can live without him," she said. "He made me feel like a lady. I've been nothing but a prostitute since I was sixteen and he treated me just like I was a lady."

This attitude surprised me. I had never thought of a call girl as a humble or ashamed person. "You don't understand," Milly said. "If you can do other things, like you can, then it's fine to do it on the side. But when you can't do nothing else, then you're ashamed." That seemed more plausible. Since I had never considered sex to be one of the finer arts, it would be sad to have no other talents.

There had been, in fact, a time when I rejected the idea of sex completely. My family history was conducive to this—I had learned "the facts of life" in a series of rather appalling ways. Since I was a highly analytical child it didn't suffice when Nonnie told me babies were dropped through the chimney of the hospital. I wanted to know how they got into the chimney and how the doctors took them out, and why they used forceps to get them out, and, as a result, for several months I had women and chimneys confused. When the situation became too impossible I was told that chimneys had no part of it, and the chimney story was denied so emphatically that I drew the conclusion that the real truth lay in chimneys and I used to stare at them with the curiosity most children would display in peeking under a skirt.

By the time this was resolved I was so intrigued with the baby-making idea that I told Nonnie I wanted to have twelve children. I was informed there was nothing hilarious about having even one. I was told years later that I had listened to the lecture and then asked if a doctor would be present during the seed planting because I "didn't want any amateurs fooling around me." I don't recall exactly what I was told, but I do know that Nonnie said men were, in this process, absolutely necessary. And I do recall that seed planting sounded like the least pleasant process imaginable. The description made men sound pretty undesirable but it didn't affect me much—I hardly knew any men. My grandfather—Nonnie's husband—was an alcoholic and very remote to me drunk or sober. My father was a shadowy figure in my life, scarcely distinguishable from any other big man with a hat and a cigar. But I decided that if men were necessary I'd just give up the idea of ever having a baby. I predicted correctly about that—I never had a baby. But I would never have guessed how many amateurs there would be in my life.

Summer school opened the Monday after graduation and again I felt lost in a nightmare of disorganization. In addition to our own students we had others from the public schools who wanted to make up flunked courses, and they brought their friends and their friends brought their dogs, bongo drums, motor scooters, pea shooters and dice. The friends of the students drag-raced up and down the alley, wandered in and out of classrooms and devised a game in the back alley involving a bull whip and a line of the school's milk bottles and much tinkling of broken glass. The road was being torn up in front of Griffin and noisy machinery and piles of sand and stone were everywhere. Then the laying of a new surface was begun with different types of noisy machines and everybody left school to watch the workmen. It was hot and if I opened the windows showers of powdery dirt blew in and coated the classroom with a thick, gritty gray layer and the machinery drowned out my voice and if

I closed the windows the room became stifling and there was much leaving to take salt tablets, a trip from which no one ever returned.

In the mornings I taught my regular classes and at noon I was assigned to police the door of the lunchroom and keep the multitudes of guests out. In the afternoon I taught an assortment of classes including Civics II and biology. The advanced civics course called for a mock election which required making ballots, a ballot box, election posters, VOTE HERE signs, campaign literature and so forth, and we spent a good part of the summer doing simple crafts with crayons and poster paint and going out to get shirt boards from the Chinese laundry, decorating a student's convertible to carry the new "president," holding caucuses and a primary and devising campaign slogans and songs. In the biology course I again followed the course manual, which led to a leaf hunt in the park during which oaks, maples, English elms and two old derelicts having an affair in the bushes were discovered. The laboratory work called for dissection of various pickled fauna from a biological supply house, including eels and a few frogs and, for reasons known only to the author of the Biology Manual, gigantic sheep's eyes; and in lieu of a term paper they were to make an illustrated notebook of animals and for one week we cut colored pictures of lions and tigers and chipmunks from magazines and pasted them on notebook paper and then copied what the encyclopedia had to say about them.

No doubt from pure frustration I developed a virus infection that hung on all summer and kept me dizzy and weak and feverish. By the end of the day I was pale and quivering and nauseated, and by the end of the summer I was inclined to have hysterical fits of weeping that didn't always begin after I got home. Twice I sat in front of the apartment and pounded on the steering wheel and cried and raged, to the vast interest of the Spanish neighbors and their dogs and children, all of whom gathered around to watch. Once Wally came over in the late afternoon and found me, red-eyed and limp from a tantrum, drinking black coffee and rum from a cream pitcher because every cup in the house was dirty. "I'm so discouraged," I said, "that I want to die." "Can't you get away for a while?" Wally asked. "You've got a week between summer school and the new term. Tell Holt you want a vacation." "That's another thing," I said. "I can't stand any more of that. If I'm going to do menial work it will be for a good cause. I'm getting out of the geisha business."

The first week of August we had a heat wave and I reacted to it by getting weaker and more hysterical than ever and I told Holt I couldn't see him again. It was a hot night and we had been at the Pump Room and I was suddenly overwhelmed with distaste for wearing tight shoes and being bored and being polite, and when he asked me for an explanation I simply said, "Because there are many things that are unpleasant that I have to do, but they're for a purpose and this has no purpose." I went home and took the phone off the hook and I felt vastly relieved. And the next day I was sufficiently bolstered to walk into Jane's office and say, "Miss Jane, just what are my chances for a raise?"

"There is a little money problem," Jane said. "It seems that for another year we shall have a money problem and . . ." I walked out.

That night at Nell's I said, "I'm not seeing Holt again because he bores me to death and Jane isn't going to change a thing at Griffin." "It may be none of my business about Holt," Nell said, "but I think he was very nice to you and it seems that you could have worked something out. After all, you are quitting Griffin, aren't you?" "No," I said. "I can't quit because I've started work with too many children and it would just be lost if I quit. I'll have to stay another year." "I just don't understand you," Nell said, and I replied, "No, you don't, and that's our trouble."

At home, I found Ann going through her clothes. "I'm

going to go to Europe," she said. "You're going to Europe? How can you go to Europe?" "It isn't that complicated," Ann said. "I'm taking an overseas job."

"How soon will you be gone?" I asked Ann when I left the next morning. "In a week or so," she said, "why?" "Because I'm not going to sit here and watch you pack," I said. "Life is a series of doors closing behind people and I don't like to be the one to close them; in that respect I'm a complete coward."

I called California at 9 A.M. and talked to both the Los Angeles and San Francisco school boards; both would require a complicated series of affidavits and recommendations and I wouldn't be able to teach for over a month, which meant starting the term late. I called New York and they said to bring my transcripts and I could take the exam on Monday; if I passed it I would get an immediate assignment. It was not quite ten o'clock when I called TWA and reserved a seat for seven that evening.

"You're the most efficient businesswoman I've ever known," Ann had told me once. This time my business sense got me through finding a city where I could teach and a plane reservation to get me there. But there it ended.

I called the movers who had helped us move in and asked them to come right over to take the furniture to Nell's basement, and I began to pack my clothes.

At noon the movers came. *"Lord,"* one of them said, resting at the top of the stairs, "you say once you get all that stuff up here you gonna stay ten years." "I know," I said, "I really thought we'd be here that long." I made a pile of summer clothes in the living room and attached a note asking Nell to put them in a storage closet. The five suitcases were filled and I walked aimlessly around the apartment, looking at the things I couldn't possibly take with me. Some time during the afternoon I cleared the refrigerator, packed what was left in the medicine cabinet and took down the draperies. In moving my Queen Anne desk a leg came off; two picture frames cracked and one of the Ming vases broke when the books were taken from the shelves. I noticed that the backs of the leather-bound Oscar Wilde's *Fairy Tales* had come loose when one of the workers threw it in a barrel.

At five o'clock the movers left and I made a final check of the apartment. My spice and tea collections I left for John and Don to use or throw away along with cans and jars in the pantry. The antique doorknobs, Victorian fixtures in the bathroom and kitchen, and shelves and lighting in the nooks were left behind. I filled the trash with old letters, Griffin themes and University of Chicago pamphlets; in clearing out drawers I found one of Ann's short stories, "The Wind Flower," and I packed it in the last suitcase. The apartment was getting dark when I dressed to go to the airport, called for a cab and finally called the telephone company to shut off our service.

After the driver carried the last group of suitcases and boxes downstairs I went through the apartment, turning off lights, checking the gas and closing windows. The darkening living room still smelled faintly of wood smoke and garlic, of Arpege and incense and candle wax and books and home. I left quickly. I gave my set of keys to John and as I walked past him and down the stairs I thought, And this is another bridge burned and I may regret it later but now I can't seem to regret anything or feel anything and perhaps that's the best way to have all this end.

I called Nell from the airport. "You certainly have left me in a mess," she said. "They just brought *piles* of your stuff upstairs, and all those damned antiques you had to have, and just what am I supposed to do with all this mess?"

In the waiting room I sat next to a very young girl who was traveling with three children. The infant cried constantly, the toddler sat on the floor and the four-year-old ran in circles around our bench. "Hi, apple pie," he said when he stood in front of me. He ran around the other direction and came back. "Hi, apple pie." His mother caught him as he ran past counterclockwise. "Don't bother the lady," she whispered to him. "I ain't botherin' the lady," he said, which was a gross untruth. "Hi, apple pie." He started around clockwise.

"I'm sorry," his mother said, "we've been traveling since six this morning and he's tired." The child on the floor grabbed her skirt and pulled himself up and then sat down heavily. He began to cry and the infant choked and wailed. "That's all right," I said, "I'm used to children." "Do you have any?" she asked. "No," I said. I could have added, And I don't have a husband, or a home; I've just thrown a lifetime collection of possessions in a basement, I've managed to alienate my family and the few people in my life and at the moment I don't give a damn.

The child ran around in front of me and stopped to pant. "Hi, apple pie." He was so exhausted he had difficulty saying it and was too stubborn to stop. The one on the floor wept into the woman's skirt and wiped his snuffling nose. And I don't want any children, I thought, and I don't want to ever start another home, and if I were Catholic or Buddhist I'd join a convent because I don't want to even bother with clothes and decisions and personal relationships.

"I wish I could make him stop," the mother was saying to me. "I'm afraid he'll get sick if he keeps running like that." It was fifteen minutes until plane time. "I'll take him over for a soda," I offered, and instantly regretted it. I was tired and distracted and I didn't want a soda and I didn't want to be with an untrained child. "That would be nice," she said. When he ran around the next time I caught him and hauled him off for a soda and left her with the two little ones.

On the plane I alternately held her infant, which I didn't want to do, and walked up and down the aisle with the four-year-old, which I didn't want to do, and occasionally I thought, Which is worse. Once she asked me if I were going to New York to live. "No," I said automatically. "Oh," she said. "Do you live in Chicago?" she asked. I told her the Maywood Street address. "It's lovely around there," she said. "Do you live alone?" Oh, *God,* I thought, why didn't I say I live in New York? "Yes," I said, "I live alone."

It occurred to me that if I had said I lived in New York I'd have had no idea where to say I lived. I had no plans at all. Ann and I had stayed at the St. Moritz one spring; I didn't want to go back there. I looked at my watch; the plane would be landing in an hour. "My husband's meeting me," she said. "Is someone meeting you?" "Yes," I said before I thought. I had never flown into a city alone and *not* been met. "I'm glad," she said. "I'd hate to be in New York alone."

Once my bags were in the cab I had to make a decision about where I was going, and I found I couldn't think clearly. Holt and I had made one trip to New York and stayed at a little hotel that faced the park. I supposed it was Central Park but I couldn't think of the name of *that* hotel. I asked the driver if he knew of a centrally located hotel. "What do you mean by centrally located?" he asked. "I don't know what I mean," I said. "I suppose I mean in the middle of Manhattan." "Well," he said, "you could stay at the Barbizon but there's nothing but women there. You can't have your boy friend in there." "I'm not accustomed to having men in my hotel room," I said. "Take me to the Barbizon." We drove in silence. "Do you mind me asking what you do?" he asked finally. "I'm a schoolteacher," I said. "I thought so," he replied.

After I signed the register at the Barbizon the desk clerk had the same curiosity. "Where do you teach?" he asked after I told him what I did. "I don't know," I said. He gave me a startled look. "I mean," I added, "that I haven't been assigned yet."

The room was a tiny cubicle with two even tinier windows, a virginally narrow bed that would have precluded entertainment if the management hadn't, a dresser, a desk and a doll-sized rocking chair. The bed and chair were draped with chintz in a violent pink rose pattern. My suitcases filled the floor space completely, a hatbox took up the chair, and I climbed across to the bed and sat down. The room was on the fourth floor and my windows directly faced what must have been an office building. I sat for a while looking at the unlighted windows across the street and then called room service for tea.

"It's too late for the dining room," the desk clerk said, "but if you're sick I can get the drug store to deliver." "I'm sick," I said.

In slightly less than an hour the tea arrived; if I hadn't been genuinely sick before, I was after I drank it. During the interim hour there had been three calls concerning the way I wanted the tea brewed, garnished and served; when it finally arrived the confusion had resulted in a mess that included milk, sugar and lemon, two floating tea bags and some bobbing bits that seemed to be from the pasteboard carton. I drank some and poured the rest down the tiny sink in the corner, unpacked the overnight case until I found a bottle of aspirin, took two, lay down and stared at the slightly swaying overhead light fixture.

I wondered if I should have taken the Victorian light fixtures from our apartment. I wondered if some day I might have wanted them again. I wondered if I couldn't have packed a little of the orange-spice tea in the corner of a suitcase and have used hot water from the tap. The picture of brewing tea at the tiny sink was unencouraging. I wondered about the people who spend their lives in tiny rooms and make tea at tiny sinks; I wondered why I hadn't stopped to eat all day and I wondered how I could possibly have failed so utterly. . . .

Chapter 8

THE NEXT MORNING I took a cab to Brooklyn, passed the teacher's qualifying examination and returned to the Barbizon. The neighborhood was completely unfamiliar to me and I was lost without my car; at six I dressed and went out to find a place for dinner, wandered around rather aimlessly and got lost twice, and finally settled for the Barbizon dining room.

The dining room was large, dimly lighted and filled with very old ladies wearing furs and artificial violets and Yardley's Lavender. The elderly lady I shared a table with had a pink rosebud in the middle of her violets and one of her sables rested on the table; its glass eyes were slightly loose, giving a cross-eyed effect, and the old lady was drinking a Manhattan and feeling very social and she wanted to talk.

"I eat here every night," she told me, "and I live on eleven and the halibut is perfectly delicious; I had some last night, and I'm having it again this evening." She shifted her furs and the other cockeyed sable lay next to her Manhattan. "I have two drinks before dinner," she explained, stroking the little corpse. "Doctor says it's the only thing for the heart, and then before bed I have wine." She crossed her legs and the table gave an alarming lurch. "Oh, I *am* sorry," she apologized, "this is the *loose* table, and I always forget. See"—she demonstrated by uncrossing her legs, and the table swayed and tilted on its one short leg—"it's just like on ship!

"Do you live here?" she asked. "No," I said, "I'm staying here until I can find an apartment." I reached for my water and the movement rocked the table toward her and we both clutched our water glasses to steady them. "Just like on ship!" she said gaily. "Have you been to Europe?" "No," I said. "I haven't."

The waitress stopped at our table. "Have halibut," my companion suggested. "I'm having halibut; it's just perfectly delicious here." I couldn't recall just what halibut was like; I couldn't remember ever cooking any. "It's really delicious," she repeated. "I'll have halibut," I said.

"Mr. Feld and I used to go to Europe every other year," she began when the waitress left. I had a strong desire to get up and run like hell and leave her with her halibut and her Manhattan and her memories of Mr. Feld and Europe. Instead I said, "How interesting. Where did you go in Europe?" "Well," she said, settling back in her chair and causing the table to all but collapse, "that was one of our little jokes. You see, Mr. Feld liked to go to London and I liked to go to Paris. So we would compromise and we would go to London first, and then we'd go to Paris. One year I said, 'Mr. Feld, wouldn't it be nice to go to Paris first this season, and to London after?' And he said . . ." The halibut arrived and we held the table down while the waitress arranged plates.

"I think," my companion said cheerfully, "that if we uncross our legs we can steady the table with our knees while we eat." We again held the table while we got our legs in place. "Now try it," she suggested. I cautiously touched the side of the table and it gave the usual lurch. "Put your knees forward a little," she said, "and it will balance the middle." I carefully slid my knees forward and we tested. It was no better. "Do you have a matchbook?" she asked. "I recall one time we folded a matchbook and put it under that short leg." I found a matchbook in my purse. "I'll hold the table," she offered, "if you can get under."

I folded the matchbook and lifted the tablecloth and crawled under the table. To my surprise I found my friend was wearing lavender hose and shoes and had very thin legs for such a heavy woman. She lifted the cloth on her side and peeked under. "How are we doing?" she asked. "It's not big enough," I said, emerging, "and the legs need a rubber thing on the bottom." "Oh, well," she said happily, "we'll just rough it!"

We attacked the little dry pieces that were apparently halibut. "I was telling you about Europe, wasn't I?" she continued. "Well, I said to Mr. Feld, 'Wouldn't it be as well if we went to Paris first, and then to London after?' And Mr. Feld thought it over and he said, "Vera, if we went to Paris first, we'd never leave, and I shouldn't get to London at all!' " She laughed heartily. "Isn't this halibut *delicious?*" she asked, whittling away at it while I held the table. "It's perfectly delicious," I answered. She held the table while I chipped at mine. I wonder, I thought, what I did with my steak knives. They were in a wooden box and I didn't see them. I wonder what happened to the pearl-handled knives. . . . I wonder where all my things are. The thought frightened me and I tried to stop thinking and remembering.

After the dessert and travelogue were over I went back to my room and tried to arrange my things. The closet was only large enough to hold the contents of one small suitcase. While I stacked the others in a corner, I wondered about Mrs. Feld. Her room is about this size, I thought. I wonder where she puts her clothes; I wonder where she hangs those little skins and how she survives on little dry pieces of halibut and how she ever takes a bath in these tiny tubs? What I was really wondering was whether I could survive for long in this way and if I would become acclimated until I could think a broken table was an adventure and dry fish was perfectly delicious and until I wouldn't care.

Maxwell Vocational High School in Brooklyn was a large, old, red brick factory of a school. On the day before school opened, when the teachers were taken for a general plant tour, I was struck with the terrible, dingy, neat ugliness of the place. My classroom on the fourth floor was one of a series of cracker-box rooms with green walls, broken desks and the inevitable prints of Lincoln and Washington, faded almost beyond recognition. After we were assigned our classrooms we broke into subgroups according to the subject we taught and went into conference rooms to order books.

"We're going to have a little problem about books, I'm afraid," the English department chairman said. "It seems we have a higher enrollment than we expected, and some of our books just plain wore out"—at this point a little group of teachers in the back, apparently a returning group from the last year, laughed politely—"and some of the new books won't be here for a while. But we'll make out," he assured us. "For the first week we'll do without books and by then we'll be straightened out. I'll go get the book lists so you'll know what's available."

"How can we teach the first week without books?" a woman sitting next to me asked when he left. An older woman behind us leaned forward. "We do it every year," she explained. "You just have them look at television and then talk about it in class." "Do they all have television sets?" the woman next to me asked. "Well, no, but the others can sit and listen for a week."

The chairman came back in with mimeographed book lists and passed them out to us. For the freshman year it listed eighty copies of *Daddy Long Legs,* a hundred and ten copies of *Giants in the Earth* and two hundred copies of a rather out-dated grammar book. I remembered the first novel from grade school; it was a sugary story of the Pollyanna vintage; the other was an involved story about Swedish pioneers in the prairie states. "Is the book listed for sophomores the same as for freshmen?" one of the men in the back asked. "Well, yes," the chairman said. "Both years use the same book." "Does the freshman class use the first half and the sopohomores the second?" the same man asked. "No," the chairman said, "the teachers just choose what they want to use." There was a pregnant silence. "Well," the man in the back finally asked, "how do you know you aren't repeating the work they've had?" "You might be," the chairman answered. "But it won't hurt them at all. You'll find these kids can use a lot of grammar."

I was assigned four senior classes and one group of sopho-mores. The first day I gave the usual assignment, to write about themselves, their ambitions, background interests and career plans. While they wrote I watched them. The classes were large—I had groups of forty to fifty—and consisted chiefly of girls. Almost to a one they wore heavy make-up with a great emphasis on eyebrow pencil, long hair in intricate curls, waves and puffs, long (down to the tops of their bobby sox) skirts and cheap, tight sweaters. I hadn't realized how fresh and pretty the Griffin girls looked. All the Maxwell girls chewed gum with a furious, intent rhythm; in the classroom they were quiet, orderly and leaden-eyed with boredom. While I explained the assignment they chewed with their mouths slightly open and their eyes slightly closed, and when I finished they opened their notebooks, uncapped their pens and began to write.

The room was deathly still and I could hear the slight scratching of their pens. I wondered about Griffin—who had come back and who was trying to teach them English and if the new teacher was as horrified by them as I had been on my first day. I remembered the story of the year before I came—there had been six or seven English teachers in one term. I wondered if the new teacher would stick it out or desert them as so many had. I wanted desperately to be back; I couldn't imagine that these coarse-looking girls could ever be as precious to me as my poor misfits had been. I suppose I'm a misfit myself, I thought, and that's why I could stand them; these robots are not what I could ever have been and I don't know what to do with them.

That night I carried home the themes from my five classes and tried to find a spot in my room where I could sit to read them. The chair was impossible; it was so small that I felt wedged in. The bed was narrow and hard and there was only one small lamp; even when I pulled it all the way over on the edge of the desk the light was insufficient for reading. I removed the shade and found that if I propped myself up in bed and twisted slightly I could read in the glare of the naked bulb. The room was stuffy and hot and the two girls in the next room were listening to a comedy program on their radio and the sound carried through their open door.

The themes were strangely alike: They were brief, neat, humorless and answered each question I had asked with a dogged exactness. The papers were set up uniformly, with their name, grade, home room, teacher's name and the date in the upper right-hand corner; the penmanship was immature but legible and they all used ink. After reading two hundred and fifty themes I knew my students had come to Maxwell because they chose either a commercial or beauty-culture course; they were chiefly Catholic and either Polish or Italian; they had boy friends, helped their mothers after school and/or worked in bakeries, dime stores or offices; they confessed they were not interested in or good at academic work, but they wanted to graduate and get good jobs, buy pretty clothes and save for furniture and wedding dresses.

They were utterly decent, honest children, hard-working and uninspired and well disciplined. They liked to type and give manicures and operate complicated switchboards. I wonder what I can teach them, I thought. They spell quite well; their grammar seems as good as can be expected with their homes and friends and I.Q.'s; they all confessed with apologetic politeness that they "hated to read" and that writing was painful. A few girls said they read "love stories" and one boy said he read two newspapers every day. I supposed that each had read *Giants in the Earth* and *Daddy Long Legs* in the freshman year and knew all about syrupy little girls who lived in the 1800's and pioneers who sat around campfires and produced babies without hot water or midwives.

I got out the book list and studied what was available for the seniors. In addition to an insufficient number of "business-English" books there was a short number of little books containing one play by G. B. Shaw and one by Shakespeare, with instructions on teaching the philosophical, technical and moral contrasts. They had had no Shakespeare up till that point even though the books were intended for college freshmen. Aside from a handful of very poor short-story collections that was the extent of available material.

When I finished mapping out a curriculum at four that morning, I could almost hear Wally saying, "Do you always have to swim upstream?" Eliminating the available texts and using library material, I had worked out a program that I thought might give the seniors an exposure to literature as a source of beauty and thought and communication. The next morning in the teachers' room I went over part of my program with another member of the English department.

"Oh, for *God's* sake," she said, "these kids won't read poetry. You want to know what I do?" I was afraid to know, but I said, "Yes." "Well, the first month I just get them *oriented*. I teach them *my* way of doing things, where to put their names on the paper, and about margins, and I give them spelling words. Then after that every week I give them ten pages of grammar and one short story and every year they have to read a book and turn in a report. You'll go nuts trying to run that program," she added. "And you'll go nuts trying to grade a bunch of papers; make it easy on yourself." "She's right," an older man put in, "these kids won't read anything and what they write *you* won't want to read. I have spelling bees and we play grammar baseball." "I've done that," the woman teacher said. "You know," she explained to me, "you draw bases on the blackboard and go down the rows and ask questions about grammar, and if they get it right it's a 'run' and if they don't they're 'out.' Didn't you ever do that?"

At the end of the first week I had fallen into a rhythmic pattern of living that involved getting up at six forty-five, taking a subway to Brooklyn, teaching until four, riding the subway back and eating dinner in the neighborhood. After dinner I would write an account of my day to Nell, try to arrange the lamp and one pillow in order to read and grade papers and at eleven take two aspirins and try not to think. And I dreaded the first weekend, when I knew my pattern would have to break.

On Friday night when I wrote to Nell I tried to explain that I still didn't know where I would be living and so I didn't know what to do about my furniture. Automatically I tried to think of a good story about where I was going that evening; after a few minutes of considering a fabricated Stork Club date I gave up and simply wrote that I was living in a small room and intended to sit in the damned room all evening and read, and that it was very hot and I hoped she was well. I'll bet she chokes on this, I thought when I sealed the envelope, which was kinder than thinking, I *wish* she'd choke on this.

By Sunday afternoon I was frantic with boredom. I tried to think of someone I knew who might be in New York, and I couldn't even think of a casual acquaintance. I remembered that when Holt and I had been in New York there had been several people who gave me their numbers, and one, a red-haired girl who Holt later said was "halfway kept" by one of the old men in his office, had told me to call her if I ever came to the city again. After much thought I came up with her name and looked in the phone book and found that she was listed. At least, I thought, as I dialed her number, I can go somewhere for dinner with her, and she can't be as bad as Mrs. Feld.

Bea Garfield's hair color had changed slightly but her personality hadn't; she was as casual and friendly as I had remembered her. She came to the door in a transparent white negligee, a drink in one hand, and said, "Come on in, I'll fix you a drink in a second, I'm on the telephone," and then went back to her conversation. "I'm sorry, baby," she said, "I had to answer the door." While she talked I looked around the room—it was very modern and hard, and black-and-white geometric prints were predominant. "Look, baby," she was saying, "I've got both bedrooms going—what the hell can I do? I can have you come over at ten but before that you'd be doing it in the hall." Oh, my Lord, I thought, I have just walked into a house of ill repute.

"I *can't*," Bea said. "I've got two girls over here now and another's on her way and if you have to have someone special you can go out and get your own." How do I get out of here, I thought, unconsciously glancing at the door, without being rude? Bea hung up the phone and turned to me. "I'm sorry," she said. "That guy just gets stubborn. He'll call up at 3 A.M. and want a certain girl and he thinks I'm going to turn the town upside down to suit him." She leaned over to the cigarette box and offered me one. "Isn't it that way?" she asked. "These fifty-dollar Johns think they're doing you such a goddam favor." Before I could answer, a door opened and a girl wrapped in a white towel came out with two glasses and walked over to the bar. "What the hell are you doing," Bea whispered as she went past, "getting married in there?"

Bea got up and went over to the bar to talk to the girl. When she comes back, I thought, I'll just say I've got a date, and wanted to see her for a moment and I'll leave.

"Maybe you shouldn't give him any more to drink," Bea said to the girl, helping her refill the ice bucket. "Any more *hell*," the girl said. "Drunk as he is what's the difference?" "Well," Bea said cheerfully, "let's make it a good strong one and maybe he'll pass out." They fussed around mixing drinks and I thought, I wonder why I'm so surprised. It's not so much different than what I was doing for Holt, it's just one step down the scale, but it seems more businesslike or something. Maybe it's just that I never saw how *we* looked.

"You know," Bea said, "I had this guy once who used to come here so damn drunk he couldn't do a thing. I used to meet him at the door with a drink and give him about three more real fast, and when he woke up I'd say, 'That was the most fun I've had all week' and take his money with one hand and shove him out the door with the other." She handed me a drink and sat down. "You just got in town?" she began, and the phone rang. As soon as she's off that phone, I thought, I'll excuse myself. If I stick around I'm certain to end up helping out in the back room, and I've retired. "In a few minutes," she was saying. "I've got a new girl here from Chicago and . . ." Oh, *God,* I thought, I should have gotten out before. What do I say to her? Does she think because I was on that deal with Holt I'd do this?

The bedroom door opened again and the girl came out and flopped on the couch. "Are you *through?*" Bea said. "I sure am," the girl said. "For the next week." The girl got up from the couch, got a towel from the bathroom and threw it in the bedroom. "Here you are, honey," she said, shutting the door and then flinging herself on the couch again. This is repulsive, I thought. This is a *whore*house and not a very high class one at that.

I took a deep breath and started to say I had to be leaving and before I could begin, the door opened and a short, drunk, red-faced man came out clutching a very small towel around his middle. "Hi," he said amiably. He weaved over and sat down heavily next to the girl, whose towel had fallen to the floor. He smiled at me and then said to Bea, "We got company, huh?" "This is Karen," Bea said. "Karen, this is Jack Westover." Jack put his arm around the girl on the couch and said, "We get along fine, don't we, honey?" "We certainly do," the girl said without conviction.

I always wondered what a whorehouse looked like, I thought. I think I had an idea of crystal chandeliers and purple velvet, but I guess a rose by any other name . . . and I've simply *got* to get out of here. They obviously think I'm a prostitute and . . . "Look honey," Bea said to him, "I don't want to rush you but I've got some people coming over." "Perfectly O.K.," he said, "I've got to pick up the wife." When he stood up all pretense of a towel was forgotten and he ambled off, stark nude, on his bowed little legs. I suppose, I thought, they're right in assuming I was a prostitute. . . . That's exactly what I was for Holt when she met me, but I wasn't an inmate of a whorehouse and I'm not doing this now and I've got to leave.

"I'm sorry I came at such a busy time," I said to Bea. "I teach in Brooklyn and I have to get up in the morning. . . ." "You do *what?*" Bea said with something akin to horror. "I teach," I said, sorry I had started it. "My *God,*" Bea said, "what about Holt Jeffers?" I give up, I thought; there's no use putting on a line for her. "He kept me," I said, "sort of, and I helped him out in his business." "Oh, well," Bea said with obvious relief. "I thought for a minute . . ."

Walking back to the Barbizon I thought, I suppose I never thought of myself as a prostitute but that's exactly what I was.

It's like the old story that if you'd do it for a million dollars you're just as much a whore as if you'd do it for two dollars, it's just a difference in salary. But I'm certain I could never have done it the way they did. They run that place like a public comfort station.

While I was dressing for bed Bea called and said, "I'm sorry we were so busy that I didn't have a minute to talk to you, but an old friend of mine from Colorado and his partner are taking me to dinner tomorrow night and I'd love to have you come with us." When I hesitated to think of an excuse she added, "This isn't business, they're just real nice people—I went to college with one and the other lived next door to me when I was married." "Well," I said, "I can't really stay out late. I do teach." "We won't," she said. "I get pretty tired running this place and I thought maybe we'd actually enjoy each other, and we'll show you New York."

Chapter 9

JUST BEFORE MY FIRST class Monday morning three little girls came into my classroom and lined up at my desk, and, when I looked up from the papers I was grading, the spokesman said, "We're a committee and I'm the chairman and would you direct the play?" She said it very flatly and with a great finality, and then they watched my face with the solemn intentness of three puppies watching their dinner being fixed. When I didn't answer immediately the plump one in the group, an Italian girl with pierced ears and ruby earrings, said, "The teacher who directed it last year is dead now." I was tempted to ask if the play had anything to do with her demise but they clearly felt this to be a serious occasion and the spokesman added, "We done a play about a girl, she writes a letter to this here sailor." "Is this the Senior play?" I asked. "No," the spokesman said, "it's the drammer-group-play." "When does the drammer-group put on its play?" I asked, and she said with logic, "Whenever the drammer-group-teacher says to." "I would be happy to be the drammer-group-teacher," I said.

They left and I thought, Well, life goes on; Friday I would have said I'd never think of these students as more than names on a seating chart and today I've become a drammer-group-teacher which is clearly a position of honor and I'm on my way to being up to my foolish neck in work and worry about them, and thank God. For although I had fully decided to make teaching in that neat, dull, unimaginative place a mechanical operation, I must have known in my heart that I couldn't hold out.

A nice, optimistic feeling lasted through the day. Behind their solemn, polite expressions I saw all the adolescent qualities that I loved so much. Twice I prodded them until they laughed at mistakes they had made instead of stammering apologies. "Oh, come *on*," I longed to say to them. "Humor grows from people's frailties as surely as roses grow from manure. Relax and don't try to be so perfect."

I got home at five thirty and at six Bea called and said, "Don't forget you're having dinner with us." I *had* forgotten and it was a jolt—I was looking forward to having dinner sent up and then going over plays in the books I'd taken from Maxwell's library. As I dressed I thought, This is why I'm glad I don't amount to anything. If I had to wear full make-up and a girdle every night, success wouldn't mean a thing.

I finally got turned out all in black and I wore the mink stole that had been one of Holt's last gifts. We went to "21." At least Nell will appreciate this, I thought, putting matchbooks in my purse. And she's the only one who appreciates it, I thought as the time and the conversation dragged on and my eyes burned from the smoke and I found myself thinking wistfully of my peaceful room. We went to three other clubs and I carefully collected small souvenirs from each place. I hope Nell saves these, I thought as I piled them on my dresser, because I'm not going out to get any more.

Somehow I began to pick up the little pieces of my life and put them back together. It was a beautiful, warm autumn and after school I started going down to Greenwich Village to look at apartments. On Saturday I went to Bloomingdale's for stockings and I found myself in the fabric section, going over drapery material and overcome with the old nest-building urge. On the plane from Chicago I had promised myself I'd never again become burdened with possessions, cats, people or hopes, and yet here I was making plans and believing that I had a *purpose* again and it was perfectly wonderful.

One night when I was down in the Village I found exactly the apartment I wanted, a studio with a skylight and a wood-burning fireplace. "Do you allow cats?" I asked the old woman who was showing the apartments. "I have seven of them myself," she said. I had noticed a familiar scent as we came upstairs. Well, here goes with the incense pots, I thought. "I'll take it," I said to her. "You'll love it here," she said while I made out the check. "You can use the little garden down back—that's where I let my cats out during the day—and there's almost no problem with leaking in through the ceiling and you can borrow a couple of my buckets just in case." "That's very kind of you," I said. "May I borrow a yardstick from you to measure for draperies?" "Of course," she said. "I'll help you."

I had dinner in a little outdoor café that was actually a half-converted back yard and drank too much wine and drew room plans on a scrap of paper and fed the restaurant cat which sat in my lap while I ate. That apartment is no doubt a terrible mistake, I thought, but it's what I've imagined a studio in Paris would be, and anyway I feel alive again.

Back at the hotel I had two messages—Nell had called at three and Bea Garfield at three thirty. I called Nell and said, "I've just found the perfect apartment." "Oh, my *God*," she said. "I was afraid of that. Couldn't you have taken a little furnished place? Who knows—you might get married." "I know damn well I'm not getting married," I said, "and I can't live in a furnished place. I want my own furniture and my books." "What about the man you had dinner with the other night?" Nell asked. "The man who took you to the '21.' " "Well, what about him?" I said. "He was middle-aged and dull and smoked a cigar." "Wasn't he interesting at *all?*" Nell said. "Wasn't it better than not going out at *all?*" "No," I said. "It was very dull and I'm not going out with him again." "Well," Nell said, "it's your life, but I do get discouraged sometimes."

"Come on over," Bea said when I returned her call. "Just come over for a couple of minutes and have some champagne." "I've had too much wine now," I said, "my knees are weak." "They'll be weaker when you drink this stuff," she said. "Come on." "O.K.," I said, "I'm celebrating anyway." I'll bet she's got men over there, I thought as I dressed, but I'm not in that business and I'm not dressing for them. I took off my high heels and put on flats, a sweater and skirt and an ancient leather coat that I used to wear at the cottage. I'll bet I'm unattractive enough that they'll let me alone, I thought when I got a glimpse of myself in the hall mirror.

The moment I walked into Bea's apartment I sensed a tense situation. Bea was frankly drunk and unaware of the uncomfortable atmosphere, but the two men on the couch were unpleasant and the girls seemed to dislike them. As they got up to go in the bedroom, one of the men turned to me and said, "Come on, baby, let's see what you got under that sweater." I finished my glass of champagne and as they closed the bedroom door I put on my coat and left. That's the last time I get into that, I thought as I rang for the elevator. Bea may be willing to put up with it but I can't.

While I waited for the elevator in the hall a man walked down the stairs and stared at me for a moment. "Which apartment did you come from?" he asked finally. When I told him he asked for my identification. I showed him my driver's license and he showed me his detective badge. Another man joined us and they stood looking at my license. "What do you do for a living, sister?" the taller man asked me. I showed him the rest of my identification and they took it over in the light and whispered for a moment. One of the men came out of Bea's apartment, buttoning his pants. He gave me a rather surprised look and joined them, and they argued for a moment about what to do with me. Finally the man I had talked to first came over and explained that Bea's apartment was being raided for illegal activities, that the men inside were also detectives, and while I was not involved he would appreciate it if I would step inside for a few minutes.

Back in the apartment, the blond girl who had been with the Italian detective was sitting on the couch in her pants and bra, the other two were dressed and talking to each other in a corner and Bea was mixing drinks at the bar. The men stood around rather helplessly and I had a feeling they didn't quite know what to do with us. "We'd better get their names before Charlie comes," one of them suggested finally. "What's your name?" he asked the girl in her underwear. "Zorro," she said flatly. The younger policeman looked embarrassed and the others laughed. "I have to go to the john," she said, pushing past them. "You can't!" the Italian detective said quickly. "I can't go to the *john?*" "Well," the older said, "you can't go in alone anyway." "Look, honey," she said slowly, "if you want to sit on my lap while I'm there it's all right with me."

She walked into the bathroom and started to shut the door. "At least don't shut the door," the older man said, stepping halfway into the bathroom. "Leave the door open." "Fine," she said casually. She pulled down her pants and sat. "Oh, for Chris' sake shut the door," the Italian detective said. The younger man had disappeared into the bedroom and the others looked miserable. "I wonder what's keepin' Charlie and Ed," one of them said, looking at his watch.

Bea passed drinks around. "I'd rather have beer if you've got it," the younger man said, coming from the bedroom. Bea went back to the refrigerator and got a bottle of beer. "Just what do you intend to do with us?" she asked him. He looked even more uncomfortable. "Don't worry," one of them said, sitting down with his drink. "You ever been busted before?" "No," Bea said. "You just plead guilty," he told her, "and the judge'll tell you you should be ashamed and let you go. You better open up out of this neighborhood, though," he suggested. "Too hot around here." The Italian agreed. "This is a bad neighborhood for workin'," he said amiably. "You should go by the East Forties. That's outa this district."

A few minutes after Charlie and Ed came the phone rang and it was Ronald Garfield, Bea's ex-husband, calling from across the street. Charlie answered the phone and pretended to be a drunk customer. "You can't talk to Bea," he said. "She's so goddam drunk she can' talk. You better come up here an' take care a her." "That'll get that goddam pimp up here," he said, hanging up. "We'll hang that pimp a mile high." In a matter of seconds Ronald rang the bell and Ed and the Italian detective ran out into the hall and arrested him.

I had been sitting in the room over an hour and I was anxious to get out. What can I say when I talk to them? I thought. I certainly can't give them much information. If they ask me what I was doing here what can I say? I could remember Holt telling about the time he was caught in a whorehouse and he'd turned his collar backward and said he was there on clerical duties. I wish I had a collar, I thought dismally.

I wonder, I thought, just what they do to prostitutes? I know I never worried about anything like this happening before although Holt did say he had trouble with a house detective once and had to pay him. I tried to remember what sort of laws there were about actual prostitution. I had heard of prostitutes being fined, and asked to leave communities, and being asked for pay-offs. Was it prostitutes, I wondered, that they used to tar and feather and ride out on a rail? I felt rather concerned about Bea but she didn't seem at all worried.

In fact I seemed to be the only one that was at all bothered. The little blonde, still in her pants and bra, was curled in the chair asleep. The dark-haired girl was reading and she looked up occasionally to make sarcastic comments to the detectives. Bea was getting progressively drunker and happier and was sitting in a corner with the youngest detective, who was taking notes, drinking bottle after bottle of beer, and was seemingly completely absorbed with Bea. The taller blonde was talking softly and laughing with the Italian detective in a corner. The other men were leisurely going through drawers of underwear, spilling out hatboxes and shoe bags, calling the station from time to time and drinking.

"Hey, Bea," one of them called from the bedroom, "you don't have no narcotics in here, do you?" "Of course not, honey," Bea said. "Aw, hell," the detective said to the other one, who was pulling handfuls of jewelry from a drawer and throwing it on the bed, "they don't take no dope. Let's stop foolin' around in here." "I ain't doin' this for my health," Charlie replied, holding up an entwined mess of pearl necklaces, "this is *procedure*." He pulled out another tangled rope of necklaces and threw them on the floor. "You better take one of them knives and cut the mattress open," he instructed his partner. "Aw, they didn't put no dope in the mattress," Partner protested. "Them dopes is *sneaky*," Charlie informed him, dropping brooches one by one on the floor. "They hide their dope *every place*."

The disgruntled partner pulled the bedclothes off and piled them in a corner and prepared to open the mattresses. The smoke grew thicker in the living room; I looked at my watch and it was almost twelve thirty. Without thinking, I

got up and started into the bathroom and almost made it be-
for the officious Charlie spotted me. *"Hey,"* he yelled, dropping the pile of handkerchiefs he was inspecting , "where th'
hell are you going?" "To the bathroom," I said. "Bill," he
hollered to the young detective sitting with Bea, "you go in
with her and see she don't take no dope." "Bill" looked incredulous. I had a feeling he was not accustomed to going on
raids. He took a long drink of beer and stood up unsteadily
and headed for the bathroom. "See she don't take no dope,"
Charlie repeated. He was starting on the lingerie drawers. I
went in first and the unhappy Bill followed, and when we
shut the door we were much closer than either of us had anticipated. "I'll turn my back," he said weakly.

Before we left the bathroom I got a look at myself in the
mirror. My face was gray and my eyes were bloodshot from
the smoke. "If you don't mind standing here another minute," I said to Bill, "I'd like to put some make-up on." Now
that the worst was over he was positively elated. I put on a
little lipstick and combed my hair, and as an afterthought
splashed on what I thought to be cologne from the cabinet.
"For Chris' sake," he said in surprise as a startling odor filled
the tiny bathroom, "what *is* that stuff?"

"What have you got *on?"* Bea asked when I came out.
"Nail-polish remover," I said. Ed came over and signaled for
me to come into the bathroom with him and I went back in.

"Look," he began uneasily, "them others should of let you
go before me and Charlie got here." He didn't seem to know
how to go on; it was obvious that something was wrong. "You
see," he said, "Charlie is like the boss—he's the lieutenant—
and now we got to at leas' take you down to the station."

The bathroom was stiflingly hot and the polish remover
smelled strangely like ether. "And just what will we do at the
station?" I asked. He looked down.

"Well," he said, "we'll haf to book you for loitering." He
looked terribly embarrassed. "And we'll have to fix up the

story a little about what you were doin' so that . . ." There
was a pause. "Anyway," he said lamely, "nothin'll happen to
you. You'll all get out of it." He walked out of the bathroom.
In the kitchen he picked up a knife and went into the bedroom to slit the mattresses. "Don't bother with that stuff
now," Charlie said disinterestedly. "Let's just take 'em on
down ter th' station."

The Italian detective got up from the chair in the corner
and stretched. "God Almighty," he said. "I'll be glad to get
home. It's too damn hot in here. You got a nice place here,
though," he added politely to Bea.

"Better wake th' Sleepin' Beauty up," Charlie suggested to
Bill. Again poor Bill looked agonized. He approached the
sleeping girl with caution and poked her with the end of his
finger. She jumped and sat up. "Get your hands off me, you
bastard," she said casually. The others laughed. "Getcher
clothes on," Charlie said amiably to her. "We're gonna give
you a free ride." "I been on free rides before," she said, going
into the bedroom. "Better go with her, Bill," Charlie said.
He and the Italian detective exchanged winks. Bill followed
her unwillingly. "You might lose your cherry yet," Ed called
after him. "One of these raids, you might just lose your
cherry." Charlie roared. *"Hey, Bill,"* he shouted, "don't take
too long in there! It don't take a real man more'n five minutes!" Almost immediately the bedroom door opened and the
blonde emerged, buttoning her clothes, followed by a very
red-faced Bill. "What's a matter, Bill," Charlie said, "didn't
she like you?" "He couldn't afford me," the blonde said.

On the way out the door Bea came over to me and said,
"I'll call our lawyer the minute we get to the station and he'll
come down with bail." "How long before we can get bailed
out?" the tall blonde asked the detectives in the elevator.
"Not long, honey," Ed said. "You got a thousand dollars with
you?" "I've got a thousand dollars for every nickel you've
got," she replied. "I wouldn't be surprised," Ed said without

animosity. "I wish ter hell my wife could hustle up a few bucks." "Bill's wife could," Charlie said. "She's real pretty." Bill's face turned purple. "My wife ain't pretty," Ed said, "but I guess a guy could put a bag over her face."

At the station we were seated at a long table in a brilliantly lighted room sparsely decorated with an American flag, a shoe-shining machine, WANTED posters, some spittoons and a NO SPITTING sign. The little blonde, who gave her name as Connie Desmond, curled up in her chair and promptly went back to sleep. The brunette pulled three chairs together, made a pile of coats including mine, covered her face with a newspaper and went to sleep. The tall blonde and Bea sat together and talked about Miami Beach. No one seemed worried.

We had been there over a half hour when an older uniformed policeman with a thick Irish brogue came over and announced that he would make one phone call for each of us. "Don't call anyone," Bea suggested to me. "No reason for anyone to know about this—I'll just have Harly come down with the bail and no one's the wiser." "I have to teach in the morning," I said. "Do you think we'll be out by then?" "Oh, God, I hope so," the tall blonde said, "I've got an appointment to have my hair touched up." "What time?" Bea asked her. "At eleven," she answered. "I'd go with you if it were later," Bea said, "but I'd rather get some sleep first."

We had been at the station for another hour when one of the detectives came over to us. "The newsboys are here," he said. "You better think what you want to say to them." A half-dozen shabby-looking men came in and walked around the table looking at us. One of them whispered something to the detective and the detective pointed to me.

"I understan' you're a schoolteacher," the reporter began, sitting down next to me. The other reporters had moved over and were standing around us, listening. I didn't answer.

"Look, babe," the first reporter said, "I don't know what

those detectives said to you, but we aren't going to hurt you." "Probably won't even use this story," one of the others put in. "We have to come down here, and nine-tenths of what we write up they never use. It's just we've got to turn in *something.*"

"Now, *look,*" the first reporter said, "you can at least tell us how come you girls were raided."

"We were runnin' a church benefit," the tall blonde supplied. "Aw, come *on,*" a little dark reporter said. "I was raided myself once, in a floatin' crap game." "What did yer old lady do to you?" one of them asked him. "She's supposed to be fierce," he explained to the others. "Before I was married," the dark one said. "Now, come on, girls. Tell us what happened."

"Look," the first reporter said confidentially to me, "this isn't never going to get in the papers anyway. It's just I've got to turn in *something.* Just tell me where you teach." "If you don't cooperate they'll put stuff in anyway," one suggested. "If you're a schoolteacher you don't want to have someone else's story in. Just tell us your side of it. It isn't going to get in anyway," he added.

Some time in the next hour I told them I taught at Maxwell Vocational, I had been visiting Bea Garfield, I didn't know her very well and I didn't know it was a whorehouse. At two thirty the photographers arrived and the same detective who had warned us about the reporters came in to tell us we should cover our faces. "With *what?*" Bea said. Seconds before the photographers were in the room the detective handed us a stack of paper napkins and we pulled them over our faces, making holes to see through, and fastened them with bobby pins. The photographers took pictures anyway. They stood on chairs and lay on the floor to get better angles, and they begged and cursed and pleaded with us to take the napkins off. "These pictures won't be used," they insisted. "We've just got to turn in *something.*"

It was hot in the station and under the napkin it was difficult to breathe. Bea made another hole in her napkin and
poked a cigarette in and I did the same. "Do you think they
will really use these pictures?" I asked her. "Oh, of course
not," she said. I doubted it, too. I could remember seeing
small-print "filler" items in Chicago papers that said: *Apartment raided in such and such a block; two women were released on bond of twenty-five dollars each.* It was given the
same attention as little items about workmen on construction
projects having minor injuries treated in emergency wards
and the weather on some day in 1800 and the names of people
who had their purses snatched.

"I wonder why they're taking all these pictures," I remarked
to Bea after another group had come in. "Nothing better to
do," the tall blonde said. "They're a bunch of vultures, sitting around waiting for somebody to die or be arrested." "I
wish Harly would get here," Bea said. It was after three,
then. When some of the uniformed police came in, Bea
asked them if our lawyer was out there yet. "It wouldn't do
you no good if he were," one of them said. "You can't get
out till morning." *"Why?"* I asked. "Well," he said, "you got
to have the judge set the bail so we know how much bond
you put up. That's about ten in the morning," he explained.

When the photographers were through we were led to a
paddy wagon and taken to a little basement jail beneath a
large police station. We sat in tiny cells until eight, were
led back into paddy wagons and taken to the Women's Court
Building. Harly was waiting for us there. "You," he said to
me, "are in no trouble at all so don't worry." "What will
happen?" I asked. "They'll find you Not Guilty and that will
be the end of it." "As far as you're concerned," he said to
Bea, "if you hadn't got drunk, and you hadn't let a bunch of
cops in, and you hadn't . . ." "Save the lecture for later," Bea
said. "What happens to the rest of us?" "You're the only one
that's in trouble," Harly said.

At about ten thirty we went into the court and were lined up before Judge Bushel and heard the Italian detective read the charge. It was couched in legal terminology and he read very slowly and pronounced the words carefully and stumblingly and it made very little sense until he came to the part about what had taken place in the bedroom. "One white female prisoner, giving her name as Connie Desmond, did willfully and unlawfully commit a lewd and obscene act with one female white prisoner giving her name as Virginia McManus. . . ." Connie, standing next to me, gave me a surprised look. "I'll be goddamned," she said softly. He linked the two other girls on a similar charge. Harly Levinson was standing near Bea and she pulled at his sleeve. I heard him whispering to her.

My bail was set at five hundred, and the other bonds at a thousand each. We went over to the side of the courtroom and sat on a bench to talk to Harly. "I know you kids haven't had any sleep," he said, "but I've got to go get the money, and get Ronald out, and there's a lot of red tape and papers to be signed. It'll take several hours but you know you're getting out."

It was then 11 A.M. We were taken upstairs and kept in the "bull pen," a large cell with ten or twelve other women, for five more hours. The other women were Negroes and they were all in for prostituting. With the exception of one very young girl who couldn't have been over eighteen, the women were in their forties and fifties. One, a fiftyish, very black woman with pockmarks, who couldn't have weighed less than two hundred and fifty pounds, shuffled slowly over and sat down next to me. She was wearing a green satin dress and carrying her shoes. "Gawd my feets hurt," she said, lowering herself to the bench and leaning back. She shut her eyes and breathed heavily for a minute. "How many times you been in?" she asked me, without opening her eyes. "I've never been in," I said. She opened her eyes and looked at me rather unbelievingly. "You doan look that young," she commented and returned to her labored breathing. "Dem bulls ketch you on de streets?" she asked. Bea snickered. "No," I said. "We were arrested in our apartment."

"Dat's de way to work," she sighed. "I been on de streets for thirty years, summer *and* winter." After a long pause she added, "Men, dey's gettin' so cheap nowdays dey doan even wanta pay for de room. Dey jest say, 'Kaint we do it inner *doorway?* Ise real quick.' Lord, lord, lord." The breathing became almost violent; her large bosom rose and fell.

A matron opened the cell door and ushered two tall Negro women in; they were incredibly thin and haggard and their black skins had an ashy overtone. They both staggered to the narrow bench that ran around the room and lay down; the one who collapsed closest to me was promptly sick on the floor. I turned my face toward Bea and groped for control. Up to this point I had merely been numb; I was aware of my head aching and my throat being too dry to swallow, and my eyes hurt from the smoke and lack of sleep. Now I was suddenly almost too sick to control myself. Bea lighted two cigarettes and handed me one. "Oh, *God,*" she said uncertainly, "I've always had a weak stomach. . . ." She stopped and we both smoked and kept our heads turned to the wall. We were aware that the woman was being sick again. "Dem addicts," the woman next to us breathed out, "dey doan do nuthin' but git sick once dey start." "Let's walk over to the bars," Bea said faintly. We stood in a far corner and smoked for a few minutes. "If Harly doesn't get me out of here soon," Bea said, "I'm going to be sicker than that woman." "I don't think it's possible," I said.

We went back to the bench and sat on the far side, next to the two colored women who were apparently friends and who were chatting away quite casually. They stopped talking when we sat down. Finally one of them said to me, "How long you been workin' in New York?" I didn't have the strength to argue. "I've been here three weeks," I said. "Three weeks," she said to her friend, "an' busted awreddy. Some folks doan have *no* luck." *"Tell* you," her friend said to me, "you do better to go work in Boston, now you been busted. It's nice up dere." "You know," the first one said, "I work in Boston fo' ten years, an' I never take no bust, not once. I come to New York an' I been in dis jail fifteen times in eight years." "You been in mo' than that," her friend said. "I *knows* you have." "I ain't either," she said hotly. "I been *busted* about thirty times but I beats it." *"Look here,"* her friend said. "You was in de Christmas of '55, is dat right? You was in an' got thirty days. Den after you got out I was back in, an' Easter you come in jest when I was leavin', right? An' den you was in dat June an' I stayed out in de streets dat whol' summer, and you were back twice fo' dey ever busts me again." The argument got complicated. "It doesn't seem," Bea whispered to me, "that anyone ever gets more than thirty days." "I should hope not," I said, "or they'd spend their whole lives in here."

At four o'clock we were taken downstairs and put in another paddy wagon. "Where are we going?" the tall blonde asked the matron. The matron didn't answer.

The destination turned out to be the Women's House of Detention. "My *God,*" Connie Desmond said when she saw the front of the building. "Why are we here if we're going out on bond?" A colored woman, one of the twenty packed in the tiny wagon with us, supplied the answer. "You *has* to go here, honey," she said as the wagon pulled into the back drive. "You kaint be bailed outter no other place."

Four hours later we were still sitting in the brilliantly lighted waiting room. "I know you're going out on bond," a very young matron apologized when the "procedure" began, "but you can't leave until all this is taken care of." "All this" consisted of a long processing involving showers, a medical examination, having our pictures and one fingerprint taken (for the health department records), having our money and purse articles counted and recounted and grow fewer at each count, and so forth. It was complicated by the large number of prisoners (some forty women were in the waiting room) and the inefficiency of the matrons, who wandered back and forth with cartons of coffee and stood chatting in little groups.

By the time we had been in the waiting room an hour, over half of the women started having severe withdrawal symptoms. One, recovering from a miscarriage the night before, was hemorrhaging severely; the others were violently sick. It had been ten hours since we had seen Harly and we had no idea what was happening. "Do you suppose," Bea said, "that Harly couldn't get the money from the bank?" He had taken what we thought would be sufficient identification; now we weren't certain. For the second time I approached the matron at the desk and asked her if our attorney was around. "I can't understand," she said, "why you people must be so impatient." That, apparently, was to be my answer. I started to walk back to our bench. "You people," she added, "have certainly spent enough time in jail that you don't have to worry about a few hours one way or the other." I started to answer and changed my mind.

Three more hours passed and I found my thinking was completely cloudy. The other three girls were asleep and Bea and I had stopped talking and simply sat and twisted our handkerchiefs. "Do you realize," Bea said finally, "that this has gone on for twenty-six hours?" "It actually seems longer," I said. A warrant officer in full uniform came in and handed papers to the matron at the desk, who signaled to Bea and me. "Sign this," she said, shoving papers across her desk. I tried to read it and the type blurred under the glare of the lights. "What are we signing?" I asked. "Can't you read?" she snapped. "No," I said, "I can't read." "Well, you are signing your bond," she said. When I walked back to the bench to get my coat she turned to another matron. "These addicts are a fine lot, aren't they?" she said.

We had, as it turned out, another half hour to wait while our signed bonds were sent out for more "processing." Mine was the first to clear. "I'll meet you outside," Bea said as the warrant officer started to unlock the door. "Outside *where?*" I asked. I had no faith in her getting out in less than another hour. Bea looked helpless. "I'll just stand outside," I said. The warrant officer held the final door open and I stepped into a huge marble rotunda; Harly was waiting and at the same moment we spotted each other the photographers saw me and I was completely blinded by flash bulbs. Harly grabbed my arm and covered my face with his hat. "Go over to the bar across the street," he said, leading me to the door, "and you don't have to talk to any of those bastards. I'll be over as soon as I get Bea out," he added.

Outside it was very cold and for a moment it revived me; as I started across the street two women reporters with note-books ran along side of me and the photographers tried to get in front of us. "Are you going over to the bar?" Gael Green, a tall, heavy blond girl from the *Post* asked me. The other woman, a tiny, pretty brunette from the *Mirror,* took my arm as I went into the bar. "Keep your face turned," she said. "Don't let them get pictures of you drinking."

We sat at the bar and they asked me questions and I asked them questions. My chief question to them was *why* all this attention from the papers, what had been in the papers already, why . . . "Here," one of the photographers said, handing me a folded paper. I opened it to the headline CITY SCHOOL MARM IS V-DOLL.

There was a picture of me smoking a cigarette through the hole in the paper napkin.

"Look on the inside," one of the photographers said. I looked. The story was headed MOTHER'S STATEMENT. ALWAYS KNEW HER WIRES WERE CROSSED. I closed the paper. For the first time since it had begun I felt a definite emotion: I wanted to get to a phone and I wanted to tell Nell exactly what I thought of her. It was probably fortunate that Harly, Bea and Ronald came in then.

"Oh, get the hell out of here," Harly said to the news people. "Come on," he said to me, "let's go out and have something to eat." "I'm not hungry," I said. "For God's sake, you didn't eat the crap in there, did you?" he asked. I tried to remember. "Harly," I said, "what *is* happening? What's *going* to happen?" "Nothing," he said. "You're completely out of it now." "But what about my school?" I said. "What will happen there?" "As soon as we have you acquitted you'll be cleared all the way around. And," he added, looking directly at one of the photographers who was hovering near us, "if these sons of bitches hadn't started all this mess . . ." "Aw, hell, Harly," the photographers said, "you think we do this for our health?"

At 3 A.M. Bea, Ronald and I went back to Bea's apartment. When we stepped off the elevator we spotted two men, hats tipped over their eyes, dozing on the floor in front of her door. When we approached, the one with the camera jumped up. "Just stan' there a minute," he said to me. The inevitable flashbulb went off. "Will you move so we can get into our apartment?" Ronald said. The one who was still sitting on the floor and leaning on our door pushed his hat back and looked up. "You can't get in anyway," he said. "Landlord changed the lock." "Yep," the other one said, "he did it yesterday afternoon." "You can really sue that sonofabitch," the one on the floor said. "How about givin' us a story about it? Are you gonna sue him?" "Ronald," Bea said, "just what do we do now?" "A guy says he's your uncle is across the street," the photographer said to Ronald. "He's been waitin' around to take you out to New Jersey. I'll go get him for you," he added, "if I can get just one more picture."

The sun was coming up when Ronald's Uncle Al dropped

us at Ronald's apartment in a Jersey suburb. "Just what day
is this?" Bea asked Ronald as we stumbled up the steps. "I
don't know and I don't care," Ronald said.

Three days later, after Bea was sentenced to sixty days in
the House of Detention, the brunette and I acquitted, and
the others found guilty but released, I asked Harly, "Where
do we go from here?"

At the trial the detective's story had been changed completely and they had scrupulously told the truth. The newspapers ignored the change and continued to print various
accounts of me nude, involved in sodomy, fighting the detectives and so forth. "Why did the detectives lie at the hearing?" I had asked Harly. "Well," he said, "they told you
you'd get out of it in the end." "What about the school
board?" I asked him. According to the papers the board was
having a special hearing for me. "I'm sending them a special-
delivery letter," Harly said, "and we're having the hearing
put off for a month to let things cool off." Since I had been
asked to leave the Barbizon and the hotel apparently wasn't
forwarding my mail, the newspapers were my source of information on matters like this.

"Gael Greene from the *Post* called," Harly told me, "and
wanted an exclusive interview with you. She said if you didn't
see her, she was going to print what you said after the trial."
"I don't even remember what I said after the trial," I said.
"Well, *she* does," Harly said. "She asked you what you
thought of the whole business and you used some pretty
rough language." Harly paused a moment and added, "I told
her she knew damn well she couldn't print it, but if she
could, she could make it double for me."

On Monday the papers ran a story about the school-board
meeting, which I had *not* attended and at which I had lost
my license for failure to appear. I called Harly and he said
he was sorry but the registered letter from his office hadn't
reached them in time.

"Just where *are* you going from here?" Ronald asked me.

During the week following our arrests, I had been staying in New Jersey with Ronald's new wife and their children. This had minimized my contact with the press and also, since I had been booted from the Barbizon, I didn't quite know where I should, or could, go. I was sure the landlord of the apartment I rented had seen the publicity. Now that the trial was over and my job was over and I had said unspeakable, bridge-burning things to my family via long distance, there was a problem about where I would go.

"I don't know," I said to Ronald. "I don't have any idea where I'm going." I had said the same thing to Nell on the phone that morning, and she had replied, "I know where you're going. Downhill, rapidly." Ronald was more practical. "Look," he said. "You can't teach anywhere until next year, at least. You can't go back to Chicago. The best thing for you to do is stay in New York."

That morning one of the men who had gone to dinner with Bea and me had called and asked me if I was staying in New York. He was very sympathetic and asked if he could see me again. Bea had lost her apartment and Ronald had found her another, in the East Sixties. "The landlord has another building two blocks away," Ronald had told me, "and you could get a smaller apartment there." The implication was obvious—at least while Bea was away there were people that I could see. It would give me time to think.

I went in to New York with Ronald and met the landlord and took an instant dislike to him. He was a wild-eyed old man with hair the color of dirty snow and he spoke guttural, broken English. I took the apartment but when I left I told Ronald, "I hope he doesn't hang around the building." "For God's sake," Ronald said, "do you think he's a detective?" "Of course not," I replied, "but I don't like him."

To my disgust he did hang around all the time I was moving in. He moved almost soundlessly and I would be piling things in a closet and have a strange feeling I was being watched—when I turned around he would be standing in the room. My nerves were short and after it had happened several times I asked him to get out and stay out.

He wasn't my only visitor. The man in the back apartment, a perfectly charming bachelor, had a gigantic German shepherd that came in any time the door was slightly ajar, would head for the bathroom and slurp water from the toilet. Since I was rather afraid of the dog it was necessary for the owner to come in and drag her out by the collar and he usually sat down for a neighborly chat before he left.

I had a feeling that the dog was trained to go visiting but I couldn't prove it; I learned to shut and lock the door behind me.

The man I had been out with turned out to be much nicer than I had remembered. He was a mild little man with a wife he didn't like, children that he insisted didn't particularly care for him, and an overpowering need to be appreciated.

The relationship was clearly defined—if he just stopped over at my apartment for an hour he paid a hundred dollars. If we went to dinner first he paid a hundred and fifty dollars. If we went out with clients I was paid a hundred for each one I saw, and a minimum of a hundred and fifty for the evening. Since the contact was made through Bea, I put half the money aside for her.

When Judge Bushel had sentenced Bea to sixty days he had added, "This is a woman who sells other women's bodies and I have no more respect for her than I have for a dope peddler." Ronald and I talked that over one evening and Ronald said, "That judge knows what he's saying is garbage but it's near election." "What do you mean?" I said. "Oh, hell," Ronald said. "Every woman in this business is a madam. A girl knows certain men that pay so much each and when the men ask her to bring a friend, either the friend splits the fee or gives her a date in exchange. Maybe after a woman gets too old to work she'll just let girls use her old Johns for a fee and not go out herself, but so-called madams like Bea pay other people fifty per cent as often as they take it in."

"I wonder why 'madam' has such a bad connotation," I said. "I suppose from the old 'white-slavery' stories," he said. "Some people think madams are part of gigantic rackets that spirit girls off and keep them in bondage. Actually no madam solicits a girl to work for her; it's the girls who have to go and apply and there are more girls than tricks."

I soon discovered that Ronald was right, and starting with Bea's Johns, I built my book as all books are built, by having friends of friends call me, and then hearing from their friends and so forth. It built up as naturally and quickly as a chain-letter enterprise and in a matter of weeks I had more dates than I could handle gracefully (with the snobbery that affects even a house of ill fame it was considered "indelicate" to see more than three Johns in a day) and I built a book of girls to whom I could assign dates and collect 50 per cent.

"I think it's asinine to only see three a day," I said once to Ronald when I had violated protocol and been running back and forth to hotels since nine in the morning. "You'd think that garbage collectors and hod carriers and prostitutes could carry on their business without a hierarchy and rules of etiquette and worrying about their social standing." "Well," Ronald said, "you have to realize that a good call girl just handles a few men and the men themselves expect it to be that way. They like to get to know a girl and have her available on an hour's notice for their clients and feel they kind of *own* her. After all, at fifty and a hundred a throw, how many men do you have to see?" "If I weren't seeing men what would I be *doing?*" I said. "I can't sit around *here.*"

The apartment was decidedly not conducive to relaxation

It had been furnished by the landlord's wife in what I soon discovered to be "furnished-apartment-standard" furniture, all of it painted black with an amazingly shiny black paint that never dries, imitation Oriental rugs, flowered draperies, flowered couch covers, flowered everything including prints of big bouquets with tulips and snowballs and black-eyed Susans that hung on the walls in carefully balanced groupings. "This apartment is so goddam ugly I'd rather be in hotel rooms," I said. "Oh well," Ronald said, "you may not get in the Whore's Who's Who but you'll be awfully rich."

Even with seeing an "indelicate" number of Johns per day I found it hard to fill my time.

Once a week I dutifully wrote a letter to Nell. Years before we had established a habit of writing long and almost daily letters to each other. All through college I had typed two and three pages every night, diary-fashion, and in return Nell had sent me accident clippings (to warn me about careful driving), pictures from *Vogue* to show me how I should be groomed, a great deal of information about people I didn't know and pages of advice. In my college sorority, where I was considered an uncomfortably efficient person, her daily admonitions to brush my teeth, set my alarm and put paper on the toilet seat were a standard joke. Now my letters to her simply stated that I was well, I was trying to make plans for the future and would let her know any developments, and I was sorry that my new name didn't appeal to her. Her letters to me were frequently incoherent and very bitter. At ten each morning my mail would arrive—soap coupons and ads, fliers from the local dry cleaners and the Democratic Party, an insulting note from Mr. Kouberoff, the landlord, who had come to dislike me as much as I disliked him, and a letter from Nell. If I felt in control I would open Nell's letter and read it and if I didn't I'd throw it away along with the ads and Mr. Kouberoff's note about garbage wrapping, tiptoeing after ten in the evening and silent chewing before

8 A.M. I was heartsick about my relationship at home but I couldn't think of anything to do about it.

When I first moved into the building I went out to dump my garbage and ran smack into the little old lady from upstairs. "You aren't married, are you?" she asked. "No, I'm not," I said. "Do you work?" she asked. "Yes," I said, trying to make my bag fit down in the too-full can. "I *thought* you had a career," she said cheerfully, "because you always look so nice when you go out." At this point the top part of the bag slipped and I stooped to pick up the fallen cans. "What kind of work do you do?" she continued. I thought as fast as I could under the circumstances. It was eleven on a Monday morning and I was in my bathrobe—what kind of work did people do if they didn't have to start out at eight thirty? I hadn't had my morning coffee and I felt befogged. "I'm a lawyer," I said, putting the last can in the bag. The bag tipped the other way and this time a mess of coffee grounds spilled out. "Why for goodness sake!" she said delightedly. "My son's a lawyer here. What firm are you with?" "I'm independent," I said, and was immediately aware the word was "unaffiliated." "Where is your office?" she said. "In my apartment," I said, slamming the lid on the can and making a dash for it.

Once inside the apartment I was furious with myself. Why didn't I tell her I lived on alimony? I thought. On second thought why didn't I tell her to go to hell? I got madder and madder. I don't want to be bothered with people, I thought. I wish I lived in a cave.

Chapter 10

THE FIRST WEEK IN my new apartment Ronald brought
Marcia over to see me. Marcia, he had explained, was "in the
business" but she was also interested in theater and was
studying to be an actress. After an hour with Marcia I had
learned that she was not only studying to be an actress, but
considered herself an immortal already; that she had nothing
to do with other call girls, generally, since it might hamper
her social aspirations, but felt I might be an exception; that
she came from a background she chose to forget and had
made a five-year plan for herself which included every form
of self-improvement from joining book and record clubs and
taking a Berlitz course in French to having her teeth capped;
that she felt "refinement" and "culture" to be the highest
goals and was going hell-for-leather toward them. Marcia
lived on a tight schedule and rose early six mornings a week
to read *How to Increase Your Word Power,* Emily Post, Dale
Carnegie, Shakespeare, outlines of history and literature and
art and *Reader's Digest* book condensations, and to do exer-

cises and practice diction and meditate and plan how to crash "society."

Marcia looked me over carefully and must have decided that I had latent refinement, for she asked me to dinner for the following night. "You'd better get your opera cape out of moth balls," Ronald laughed when she was gone. "I think this is going to be formal." "When does she get time to work?" I asked him. "Well," he said, "she has very set hours for that. Some of the guys are very impressed with her—she makes the scene in a trailing gown and serves champagne—the whole bit." "Is she an actress?" I asked. "God Almighty!" Ronald said. "She is *this* year. Before that she read fifty books on royalty and wanted to go to Europe and marry a count or something. She is just determined that no one will ever call her a prostitute." "Does anyone?" "That's mild," Ronald said, "to what the other girls call her."

Dinner at Marcia's was about what Ronald had expected. Marcia lived in a never-never-land apartment with white fox rugs, mirrored walls and ceilings, creaking antiques, many ornately framed and spotlighted Famous Artist prints, and gold cherubs holding lamps and ashtrays and towels. In her bedroom she turned down the brocade spread to show me satin sheets. We ate by candlelight and discussed art, and shortly after dinner, while we were sipping espresso and listening to classical music, the phone rang and one of her customers insisted on coming right over. She covered the mouthpiece with her hand and whispered to me. "He has a friend with him." "That's all right," I said. "Charles," Marcia said, "I have a dear friend of mine here who is a musical composer, and she will see your friend." "And what do I do if he asks me what I compose?" I asked Marcia while we were changing into robes. "Why, just say *contemporary* music," she suggested. "He's a very uncouth man and won't know the difference, but he pays well."

Marcia was the one who took me to Maria Archer's

beauty salon for the first time. "You should do something with your hair," she said after we had gone on several dates together. "You sound a little like my mother," I said, "and I do have it done." "It's not chic," Marcia protested. "It may be what you'd wear teaching school but it's not what a *society* woman would wear."

"I doubt that this is what a society woman would wear either," I said to Marcia when a Maria Archer operator had fixed my hair. After mourning the shortness of my hair, the operator, a nervous little homosexual with a cockney accent, had doused my hair with beer, rolled it up and again soaked me with beer. He combed it out, ratted the hair and stretched it until I had a full, bird's-nestlike edifice on my head, and then sprayed it liberally with lacquer. The result was very spongy and very little like hair but it gave the effect of a full, period hair dress.

"Of course it's what society women wear," Marcia protested. Her hair style was identical—in fact, every woman in the salon emerged in the same style. "Why do they all have their hair done in the same way?" I asked her. "Because it's chic," she said.

When I passed a photograph machine the next day I had a snapshot taken and sent it to Nell. "Very chic," she wrote. "Maybe your other style was all right for teaching school, but if you want to look chic this is much better." I had thought that she would agree with Marcia but I wanted to check.

By now Bea had been in jail nearly a month and I wrote to her and told her about working and Marcia and my struggles with the landlord and she wrote back telling me about straw-filled mattresses and bedbugs and dinners of overcooked cabbage and undercooked beans. *I'm counting the days until I get out,* she wrote. *I'm sure we can get going again and I'm looking forward to working with you.*

My God, I thought when I read the letter. Is it possible

this is going to be my life from now on? Certainly I wasn't getting any place with plans for the future; my days were so filled with boring, repetitive things—eating and dressing and shopping for shoes, going to the beauty parlor and changing my clothes for dinner and waiting for a call and then waiting for a cab—that I barely had time to write a letter to Nell. It seemed incredible. There had been a time when I could, in a day, teach five classes, go to classes of my own at the University, sew, cook, read; and now in the same amount of time I accomplished nothing important or permanent but managed to live in a hurried rat race. I won't keep this up, I thought desperately. I won't allow my life to degenerate into this. But I didn't see how I could prevent it.

The next night I had a date with a financier from Chicago. Bea had arranged it for me through Ronald. "Bea says," Ronald told me, "that he's very rich and very generous and a perfect moron." "And what does *that* mean?" I asked. "Oh, don't *worry* about it," Ronald said casually. "If he weren't safe Bea wouldn't see him." That was true. A John who in any way caused trouble, or refused to pay, or was even rude was likely to be blacklisted to a point where no reputable call girl would see him. Still, it didn't sound too promising.

I worried about it all afternoon and I asked Marcia about it when she called. "*Don't* talk about it on the *phone*," she said. "Is it *that* bad?" I asked. "Of course not," she said, "but in this city you don't discuss anything but the weather over a telephone."

I decided to go ahead on the date, but be very careful. As a child, Nell had led me to believe that white slavery was a major American business and that most strangers, and particularly janitors, candy-shop owners, bachelors and Chinamen, were engaged in it. She had told me some lurid tales about women who sat on the toilets in Chinatown restaurants, were snatched through the sliding panel and awoke in Shanghai. Nell had emphasized that although Chinatown toilets were fatal so were most other places where Strange Men and Morons lurked. As I dressed, I worried about what sort of moron J. F. Ronley might be.

When the doorbell rang I steeled myself and when I opened the door and saw a smiling, pink-cheeked, immaculately groomed, plump little man, I was surprised. I had fully expected him to have a leering face and a loose zipper. I was still on my guard. All through dinner I drew him out and found he was interested in race horses, boats, money and himself. In the theater he took my left hand and pulled and patted and mauled it in a typically male but not particularly moronic fashion, and I kept watching for the first clue to what Bea had intimated.

After the theater we went to have a nightcap at his club. After we were settled in the secluded corner of an ornate, walnut-paneled room and had ordered brandies he said, "That was a nice play. There is something about England, and the English *graciousness,* that is most appealing, don't you agree?" I agreed. I tried to glance at my watch. "The modern world," he went on, "can be most crude. Modern man can be most crude, and shocking. Now just the other day I read about a dreadful thing going on in California; there was a group there, of men and women, who were found to have a form of free love, just sleeping with each other's husbands and wives—a dreadful way to live." "That is disgusting," I said. I could see my watch and it was after midnight. "I don't suppose," he said, "that you have ever seen anything like that, have you?" "No," I said, "I haven't." The look of utter disappointment was pitiful. "Well," he said, "just what do you suppose such dreadful people would *do,* at those terrible parties?" I was tempted to say I had a very poor imagination, but I hadn't the heart to. It was beginning to be similar to a grammar-school game called simply "talking dirty." "Let's try to decide," I said, and was rewarded with a beaming smile. "Let's try to decide what kind of *awful* things they could do," I went on. "Do you suppose they take off their clothes?" "Oh, yes," he said. "I'm certain such people would. They'd just run around nude, men and women together. I imagine they swim nude, and they . . ."

When I told Marcia about it the next day she said, "Well of course when you told me who it was I knew what Bea meant by 'moronic' but I couldn't say anything on the phone." "Just who do you think is listening on my phone?" I asked. I couldn't imagine anyone wanting to hear my conversations and anyway I didn't see how they could do it. "The wire tappers," Marcia said. "The police or the FBI or the Treasury Department or anyone else who might make a buck from you." I thought that one over. "Well," I said, "if they've been listening it's too late now." "No," Marcia said, "they most likely haven't got your phone bugged yet since you've only been in the apartment a month. I'll show you a code you can use that'll bore the hell out of 'em."

Marcia's codes did make for dull conversations. She used the system the girls in Florida worked up for price ranges, talking price in terms of selling a "picture of Grant" for a fifty-dollar transaction, or a "picture of Franklin" for a hundred and so forth. Like most call girls she never discussed sex or money in any form directly on her phone. A friend of hers, a madam in the East Seventies, had a more intricate code which apparently worked, for in twenty years she had never been busted. A nervous, overcautious woman who had once been a fabulous call girl in Chicago, she ran a quiet and very efficient whorehouse in her apartment on a nearly twenty-four-hour-a-day basis, while she directed the operation from the living room and made figurines and busts of Madonnas from plaster of Paris and painted them. Some she sold to customers and many she sent to her grandchildren for gifts. Her religious bent carried over into her filing system and she kept the names, phone numbers and prices that could be charged on the odd-numbered pages of *Lives of the Saints*.

"I'm not what you'd call a religious fanatic," she told me once, "although of course I go to church, but that goddam book has brought me more luck. I could *never* keep my numbers in no other place and feel safe."

On the telephone with customers she carried on conversations about insurance policies, pretending the customer was an agent and discussing premiums (to set prices) and times of appointments in his office (meaning the time he would come to her home); sometimes she would pretend the caller was a tavern owner and go into involved discussions about the number of bottles of Scotch she would need for a party (meaning the number of girls he would need for his), and using five- and ten-dollar figures to represent fifty and a hundred. Her ingenuity was amazing. "You want to pick up the cleaning at four?" she would ask a customer. "I guess you'll want to pick up two or three skirts at least or it wouldn't be worth the trip. Oh, you don't want to come for no less than *four*—all right— I guess you must have some new assistants on that cleaning truck, you never had to get that many skirts before."

"That's the way you have to handle it," she explained. "Goddam cops, they listen to everything, but let 'em read that off in court."

I tried to develop such a system but it wasn't easy; men like the financier were determined to toss in a few juicy comments. "Terrible, terrible thing I read in the paper yesterday," he would begin. "Tell me when you see me," I'd say quickly. "Sure, sure," he would say, "I'll not take up your time now but did you ever . . ." Before I could ease him off we would have a full description of sodomy, plus, if I couldn't block it, a final "We sure had fun last night, didn't we?" After which it was rather useless for me to add, as Marcia sometimes did after such a *faux pas,* "Yes, I love going to evening services."

It was around the middle of November that Ronald came out of a night club and found a pretty, painfully thin girl who didn't look more than sixteen asleep on the front seat of his car. With some difficulty he got her awake and the girl apologized and explained that her boy friend parked cars for the club and since she had no place to go she slept in the parked cars until he was through work. The boy friend actually wasn't her boy friend at all but merely one of the few people she knew in New York, and if she couldn't find a few tricks on the street he allowed her to share his room in a flea-bag hotel and the next night, when with luck she would take in fifteen or twenty dollars at two and three dollars a throw, she would buy him a late supper and give him five dollars for the use of half his bed. According to Ronald, he was so touched that after getting absolute proof she was twenty-two he took her to the furnished but empty apartment that Bea was to occupy when she got out, sent out for food and put her to bed.

"Honest to Christ," Ronald said to me, "I didn't touch the kid. I couldn't." "I couldn't either," I said, "she's filthy." For although she had a delicate beauty she was no Eliza and didn't intend to be. Her voice had surprising depth and coarseness and her language was even more coarse. Her dream in life was a red satin dress and she intended to get one with the first money she made, despite Ronald's protests that she could become "a real call girl and not a streetwalker" if she would listen to reason and advice. Her long, honey-colored hair finally did get washed at Maria Archer's beauty salon but she bullied the operator into a corny pompador hairdress.

Awful clothes and hairdo and even dirt notwithstanding, men liked Vi. "Are you *certain* she's of age?" they'd ask in awe, and secretly believe and hope she was not. For if Vi could be intimidated sufficiently beforehand not to tell travel-ing-salesmen stories or talk about her abortions, she gave a sweetly innocent effect.

She got along less well with the other girls. "They're so damn jealous of me," she would tell me in her hoarse voice.

It wasn't true but she liked to think that they envied her freshness—she wore no make-up— Her pet peeve was Geraldine, Marcia's closest friend. "She looks like my Gram when they got through undertakin' her," she would say, loud enough for Geraldine to hear.

Geraldine did wear a fantastic amount of paint and at times she *did* looked slightly embalmed. Coming from a Brooklyn family who, according to Marcia, were "both poor and *unrefined* (people may *have* to be poor, but there's no reason for dirt and unrefinement)," Geraldine had somehow attained all the poise and suave veneer for which Marcia fought, and without any effort at all.

Geraldine lived on Sutton Place and paid over $450 a month for her apartment. She slept all day while her maid answered the phone, made appointments and cleaned; at five in the afternoon she would be awakened by the maid, have breakfast in bed, look over the two or three appointments for the early evening, and begin her make-up job.

Sitting in a strong north light and assisted by make-up lights, she would go through a routine that took between an hour and a half and two hours. After a facial with packs and saturated pads she would apply foundation quite literally in layers, sometimes brushing and sponging on five or six different shades, one a clown white, until her face was a flawless— and expressionless—mask. Since she almost never smiled and her expression was as fixed, vapid and immobile as her personality, despite the thickness it never cracked. "I'll bet under that crap she's a hundred years old," Vi said once to Marcia. And Marcia, who was torn apart with jealousy, was forced to admit that under it Geraldine was only twenty-seven and perfectly beautiful.

"Don't she ever lay up with no man for fun?" Vi asked Marcia. Vi thought that while all the girls were undersexed (she personally enjoyed every man she was with and was horrified to learn that she was the only one), Geraldine was the coldest fish of all. Marcia admitted that Geraldine had a scant personal life. Marcia herself was in and out of love constantly as were most of the girls; no paid customer, be it a movie star or other celebrity, had any real appeal. Marcia would hurry from a date with an actor known for his virility and charm to be with her Puerto Rican grocery-delivery boy, in whom she found "deep sensitivity and inner beauty" until he stole her purse. One was love and the other business. And it was rare for Marcia to like men anyway; she, like most of the women in the business, preferred other women, although her taste there was scarcely better.

Just before Thanksgiving Bea was released. With her usual good nature she accepted the fact that Vi was living in her apartment and welcomed her. "How can you put up with that?" I asked Bea on her second night out. We had been entertaining a group of men from a West Coast aircraft company at Bea's apartment and Vi had, in my opinion, made an awful fool of herself. Despite the fifty- and hundred-dollar fees she was now making, as opposed to the pitiful sums she had made before, she couldn't resist "conning" men for money. If she could cajole a man into giving her a few dollars she was elated—it meant much more to her than the larger sum. This evening she had whispered to the president of the company and asked him for "a little extra money, to buy a birthday present for my mother." Marcia, who had overheard it, was furious: Like most call girls, she proudly refused to discuss money with men and, above all, would never allow one to think she was in need of any. "I'll never work on the same party with her," Marcia had stormed to me in the bedroom. I told Bea, who played, as usual, the role of peacemaker. This very trait had built up her business; she was totally gracious and uncritical, both of the men and the girls who worked with her. "Poor Vi," she said of this incident, "she's like a pitiful kitten." "Kitten, hell," Marcia said. "She's not that young. She's a born streetwalker anyway." Which was very true, but Bea couldn't, or wouldn't, see it.

Bea's charm had made it possible for her, on her second day out of jail, to round up most of her old customers; in a week she had her business in full swing. Several years before, when she was working for Lou Hillon, then the biggest madam in New York, men had been intrigued with Bea and wanted to see her without going through Lou. Unfortunately, or fortunately, according to which side of the fence you're on, this is the way many madams lose their businesses. Polly Adler is reputed to have told her girls, "If you steal my Johns I'll send the police to your door," and thus kept her business intact. Lou threatened with police, murder and mayhem but it did her no good. Men constantly took girls' private numbers and then went directly to them. Since Lou's 50 per cent was eliminated, the men would split the difference with the girls and pay seventy-five dollars. It was said that in Lou's younger days—she had been operating in New York for forty years—she would have found some way to prevent this, but she had fallen prey to some of the classic call-girl curses: She was addicted to pills; she had formed the habit of keeping someone, and her current loves—one a homosexual boy who did female impersonations, and the other a young Lesbian— hated her, reviled her in public and kept her in a constant state of agitation and poverty.

One night Marcia, who was inclined to take pills herself, came over to my house in a sad state, bemoaning her lost virtue and the filth to which she was subjected because of men, and said, "I can't bear the thought that to earn my daily bread I must give up a woman's most sacred commodity." "I don't mean to be unsympathetic," I said, "but you gave up your most sacred commodity gratis, from what you tell me, and you have a very nice mode of living for the most part. You could earn your daily bread in many other ways if you didn't prefer having more money and more time."

"Well, so could you," Marcia retorted. "You could go work in an office." "So I could," I said, "but I don't want to. And I'm not really complaining. I hate to live this way, not doing the kind of work I feel I'm suited for, and not doing anything creative or important or permanent, but I feel the same way about typing letters for other people or filing or thinking their thoughts or doing their housework. I don't like to be a 'tool' any way you look at it, but most people have to be just that at times to make a living, and I think this is a fairly useful thing to do and it pays well and I don't have to do it eight hours a day."

Marcia didn't agree.

She went through the periods of terrible depression common to call girls and which lead so many to alcoholism, drugs and suicide. In these periods she felt defiled and degraded, and bored her friends with explanations of why she wasn't really a prostitute, etc., etc. That night at Bea's, before we went out for what is known in the business as a "marathon"—a date that includes dinner, rounds, possibly endless or seemingly so, of night clubs, and whatever else a group of drunk out-of-towners can devise—Marcia was in a deeply downcast mood and set out to show us why she wasn't a prostitute at all.

"I don't particularly care to even go on the same date with Linda," she began, referring to a girl who had recently come from Las Vegas. Her overprecise diction let me know she was in a Grand Lady mood. "I don't see why not," Vi said. "She's a whore just like the rest of us." This drew the desired result from Marcia. "I do not happen to be a *whore,*" she said coldly. "There are some of us who are doing this to support our *art.*"

Marcia contended there were three basic types of call girls—the out-and-out call girl, who built it as a business, knew nothing else and kept at it until she retired; the high-class hobo, who did just enough of it so that she never had to work, perhaps seeing one person a week and sleeping the rest of the time, or cadging small sums of money from various men or getting them to buy her clothes and meals or let her sleep at their homes for a while, preferably without going to bed with them; and the third type. And Marcia placed herself firmly in the last category, of women who worked as call girls to support themselves while becoming successful actresses, models or artists, or used it as a steppingstone to another career, a business or a wealthy husband. Ignoring the fact she had been in the business eight years and was no actress anyway, Marcia thought of her prostitution as a sacrifice made to the theater.

"Well, if you ain't a whore I'd like to know what you are," Vi said, knowing exactly what Marcia would say and enjoying it thoroughly. I also knew what Marcia would say and I went into the other room and let them fight it out.

That evening we were entertaining a group of Southern buyers. We had been warned it would be a nightmare and it was. They took us to dinner, at Broadway Joe's because they had heard about it, and then on a round of clubs that included an Oriental Room with little Jewish waiters in Chinese getups and a floor show of Irish girls, in heavy sloe-eye make-up and flowing cheap black wigs, doing hulas with bumps and grinds. We sat through a female-impersonation show at a small clip joint with some hard-faced, obviously male dancers in elaborated, basted-together costumes of satin with piles of shedding furs and feathers. They wobbled on their high heels and made constant wig and falsie adjustments while they danced. We tried to watch a floor show from the worst possible seats in the Latin Quarter and then went on to a club where we had missed the last show and so just sat and drank watered drinks and watched the waiters changing tablecloths and looking at their watches. After several more warm, tap-water drinks in the visitors' hotel suite we went out into the rain for the tenth time to get a cab. It was after five.

I dropped Bea off at her apartment and went on to my own. As exhausted as I was when I got home, I noticed something was amiss. The bed, which I had made in the morning, was askew as though someone had been sitting on it, a desk drawer was slightly open and a pile of clothes that had been on a chair were on the floor. I looked in the closet and behind the shower curtain, the only possible hiding places in the apartment, and of course found no one, but I was worried.

"You need a vacation," Ronald said when I told him the next day. "With the kinds of locks you've got how could anyone get in? Anyway," he added rudely, "the way you keep house if an elephant had been in the middle of the room you wouldn't find out for a week."

In the afternoon I went over to see Linda, who had a suite at the Park Sheraton for the week she was in town but had no particular assurance she could pay for it. Linda fitted perfectly into Marcia's high-class-hobo group; she traveled about with an extensive wardrobe, furs and jewels and no money. She would stay in Las Vegas as long as some man was winning and would give her money, then find one coming to New York who would pay for her plane ticket and the extra weight on her clothes and away she would go. Once in another city she would check into the best hotel and call up a few of her old Johns. Unfortunately for the hotel, the money she earned would go for clothes and only if some man would come to the rescue for the hotel bill would it be paid. We sat and drank cocktails sent up via room service, admired her new shoes (the $200 from the night before having gone into $200 worth of footwear as soon as I. Miller's opened) and at four I went home to dress for a dinner date.

My venetian blinds were half-opened and on an angle. "God Almighty," Ronald said on the phone. "*No*, I haven't been in your apartment and no one else has. What have you been drinking?"

I fixed the blinds and then I noticed my wastebasket was

empty. I called Ronald back and triumphantly told him that six letters from Nell that I had put in the basket just before I went to Linda's were missing. "I wouldn't be surprised if the Lord took pity on your messy apartment and sent an angel down to dump the trash," he said. "Anyway," he said seriously, "who would want your mother's letters?"

That night when a man who was a friend of Linda's from the garment district came over, I developed a fear that someone was looking in my window. The apartment was on the ground floor and at first the footsteps going past my windows had bothered me, but I had learned to ignore it. Now I was certain that I could see shadows, indicating that someone was very close to the window, and the bushes rustled; it was all I could do to get through the evening.

"Do you think it could have been a detective?" I asked Marcia. "I don't think so," she said. "I don't think anyone would dare look in a window in full view of the street." It seemed logical but the next morning I found footprints in the bushes.

"When the janitor took the screens down he could have left the prints," Bea said. "It's rained since," I said.

And when I came home from the beauty parlor several bottles of pills were uncapped and a new bottle of rum was half-emptied. Marcia was with me and she treated it casually. "Let's finish the rest of the bottle since your gremlin started it," she said. "Do you want the rest of the vitamin pills the gremlin left open?" I asked her. "You are getting neurotic," she said seriously. "You aren't going crazy, because people as neurotic as you are never go crazy, but you are getting mildly screwy." Marcia had a way of combining terms from her self-improvement texts with her own vernacular and coming up with some incredible things, but for once I agreed with her. I was too neurotic to ever lose my mind.

We were very much into winter now and both Bea's and my apartments were cold. Since we had the same landlord, we went together to complain and the result was negative. We were simply told the apartments were not cold. I went out and bought a thermometer and set it up in the middle of the room and when it registered 57° in mid-afternoon I called Mr. Kouberoff and invited him to come over and see it. The reply was a five-minute monologue during which I held the phone far from my ear and finally put it on the floor to soften the blast of Russian-American oaths and curses and insults.

I called Bea and she said, "Come on over here. I think it's a little warmer." I went over and it wasn't—Bea had simply worked out a more ingenious warming suit—she wore a night-gown as a base and had piled on sweaters and a scarf and a jacket and two pairs of sox, but the tip of her nose was de-cidedly blue. I had brought my thermometer, and placed it in the bedroom. It registered 58°, which was slight improve-ment. We were trying to devise a way to prove the tempera-ture to the housing commissioner when the phone in the living room rang. "It's Dave Crawform," Bea said, coming back into the bedroom. "He'll be over in fifteen minutes." "You can't see him like that," I said. "He wants to see both of us," Bea replied, "and you don't look much better." I had put on one of Ronald's navy pea jackets, turned up the collar, and I *didn't* look any better.

Bea got out two very filmy negligees. "When the doorbell rings," she said, "we'll pull off our clothes and dive into these."

Negligees were Bea's idea of properly sexy attire. Marcia was likely to greet her Johns in any one of a number of out-landish costumes—velvet slacks, balloon-sleeved blouses and high heels, black-lace nightgowns, a brocade dressing gown and gold slippers. One call girl in the East Seventies always dressed as though she were going out for the evening, and greeted the man in a cocktail dress and a fur wrap, then promptly dropped the whole outfit and got down to business. Another, a call girl and madam, went around in a full skirt and scoop-necked evening sweater, and when she went into the bedroom with a John she didn't take her clothes off—as she herself put it, "No need to strip for a John, just kick off your shoes and pull up your skirt and get it done." One girl wore old dirty blue jeans around her apartment and a shirt with the tail out and went barefoot. Vi wandered around Bea's nude if it was hot in the house, and in slacks and her boy friend's old lumber jacket if it was cold. The crowd from the Village wore whatever they had that was new—regardless of how inappropriate it might be for the moment. I usually wore slacks and a sweater. But Bea stuck rigidly to the idea that a man expected a girl to look lacy and wedding-nightish. "I'll freeze in that," I protested. "You'll put it on," Bea said firmly. "When the bell rings we'll just jump into the robes."

We did just that and both came down with colds by the next morning. I stayed in bed in my cold apartment under a pile of blankets with a scarf around my head and cursed Kouberoff. Bea called at noon and said she was too cold and sick to get up and if I would come over with some Campbell's chicken soup and tea I could share her cold pills.

When I left my apartment, Mr. Kouberoff was standing directly across the sidewalk from my windows, leaning against a tree. We didn't speak.

"Isn't it strange for him to be standing out there in the cold?" I asked Bea. "I wouldn't think anything that old bastard did was strange," Bea said. "Heat some soup."

When Ronald came I told him about it and he said, "For Christ's sake, can't the old buzzard even sit in a tree without you worrying about him?" "I wasn't afraid he'd freeze," I said. "I think he's watching my apartment." "Do you know what p-a-r-a-n-o-i-d means?" Ronald asked me. "Yes, I know what paranoid means," I said, "but it doesn't mean there aren't any blackmailers in the world."

In the afternoon Linda came over, bringing a friend who had just come in from Miami. Her friend, whose name was

Lucille, had all the requirements of a group-two call girl: She had a new, full-length Autumn Haze mink coat, a suite at the Waldorf and fifty cents in cash. Linda wanted Bea to put her to work.

They bought a stack of new movie magazines and sat on my bed to read them.

"Hey, Lin," Lucille said after a few minutes. "Get a load of this." "God," Linda said. Lucille showed me a full-page color picture of a rather insipid starlet pulling taffy with an effeminate-looking blond boy on the other end. "Lin an' I used to hustle in Vegas with that broad," Lucille said. "An' she was th' dirtiest broad I *ever* worked with," Linda added. "She wore black underwear because she said the dirt didn't show." "Can you see her pullin' taffy?" Lucille laughed. "That's sure a switch." They went back to their individual magazines and I tried to go to sleep.

"Look at this," Lucille said again. She held up a picture of a male star with his two-year-old son. The caption ran, *Daddy, why can't ice cream talk?* and in smaller print was the answer, *Because, honey, words are just for people. Words are for Mommy and Daddy to tell you how much we love you: and for saying Hello in the morning; and for saying Happy Birthday. Words are only for people, so they can make each other happy.*

"*Jesus!*" Linda said flatly. "I'da told the kid because it's food and to shut up and eat it." "That's not the *point*," Lucille said. "The point is can you imagine them pretendin' that guy ever said anything like that? He was one of our tricks," she explained to me, "an' he's one of the cheapest, dirty-mouth bastards in Hollywood." "Yeah," Linda added, "you remember the time he tried to get you down to thirty-five because he says he's got a buncha kids?" She turned to me. "Lucille looks at him," she continued, "an' she says, 'If you'd go home to that buck-tooth wife of yours you'd save th' thirty-five an' you could make some more kids.'" "He paid the

fifty," Lucille added. "He's the *dirtiest*." They returned to
their reading.

For the next two days Bea and I stayed wrapped up in bed,
jumping into negligees only when the doorbell rang. The
third day our colds were better and I could feel my ambition
returning. "You know," I said to Bea, "my lease calls for
decorating. Do you suppose I could get Kouberoff to do it in
time for Christmas?" The idea of spending Christmas in a
chilly apartment, alone and looking at four dirty ivory walls,
was worrying me. I had an idea if it could be freshly decorated, and I got a few of my pictures and books from home—
"Go down and ask him," was Bea's muffled reply. The thermometer was still in the fifties and we were talking through
our blankets.

I went down to Kouberoff's office and came back feeling
I had been compromised but something had been accomplished. "He says," I told Bea, "that he won't decorate it but
he'll give me the paint." "That's a violation of the lease,"
Bea protested. "I know," I said, crawling back under the
covers, "and so is this temperature, but it's better than nothing."

"I've got some friends in the Village that'll do it for a few
dollars," Marcia said that night. Marcia had a number of
"friends in the Village" who were on the bottom of the high-
class-hobo group. A group of Lesbians, they lived from hand
to mouth, being kept by strippers, hustling when absolutely
necessary, putting on shows and so forth. "Don't talk her into
that," Bea said. "I'd never have them in my house again."

I had heard about Bea's last experience with them. One
of their chief faults was casual, admitted stealing—which they
euphemistically referred to as "swinging with things"—and
playing practical jokes. According to Bea, they had never
come in her house without filling their pockets; they stole
for the pure joy of stealing and often took things that could
be of no use to them, such as Bea's honor society and sorority

pins. One, a little blonde who worked very infrequently but was much in demand, had written four-letter words all over Bea's pillow case and sheets the last time she worked.

"I'd never have them in my house again," Bea repeated. "Nuts," Marcia said bluntly. "We all use them when they'll work—let's face it." "Well," Bea said honestly, "that's true I guess, but you have to watch them every minute."

The two that Marcia sent over to decorate for me were Nicki and her new girl friend, Anthea. They were saving money to go to Europe, but as fast as they earned it they blew it on custom-made sports clothes— "Can you *imagine* custom clothes, living in that flea-bag hotel?" Marcia had said disgustedly—but now they were going to save their money, go to Paris, pick up wealthy women in the gay bars and amass fortunes. Toward this end they had decided to do any kind of work to get one-way tickets to France, counting on the wealthy women there to take over upon their arrival. Painting my apartment was their first project and they came in bubbling with enthusiasm. The enthusiasm lasted a few hours; they dragged a paint brush for three more mornings and managed to streak one wall, and then they went back to the peace and marijuana of their hotel room, taking with them several of my white shirts, a corduroy jacket I intended to throw away and a couple of books on Educational Philosophy.

"What will they do with my education books?" I asked Marcia while we were painting the walls.

"Add them to their collection of Useless Stolen Items," she said.

We finished the painting in one day and the next morning I started out to the beauty parlor and found Mr. Kouberoff leaning against the tree across from my windows.

"You finish the painting?" he asked cheerfully. "Yes," I said. He came over to me. "Well, I'm gonna tell you something," he said. "Dat paint, it's a gonna turn ivory." "Why?"

I asked. "Because," he said, "dat's same paint I use to make iv'ry walls, dat's why." "Why didn't you tell me?" I said. He smiled nastily.

I rushed back into the apartment and, sure enough, around the edges the yellowish tone was beginning to show. I called Bea and she said, "I had paint that did that once and I got my money back from the store. Call Harly and ask him what to do."

Harly thought it was hilarious. "Why, that old bastard sounds like something from an old-time melodrama," he laughed. "That's really very, very funny." "Isn't there anything you can do about it?" I asked. "Well," he said, "you can just get some decent white paint and go over it. Make Bea help you." "I don't mean that," I said. "Can't something be done to him?" "Sure. What's his first name?" "Vatchoo, I think." "Sounds like a sneeze," Harly commented. "Well, you call his home in the middle of the night and when his wife answers you say, 'Is Vatchy there?' and when she says he's asleep, you say, 'Well, this must be his housekeeper. Please give Vatchy the message that the girl he sees two nights a week is still waiting for him, and he has to pay the fifty dollars anyway!' That'll fix him at home."

"What about fixing my walls?" I asked. "Oh, hell, get Bea to help you repaint," Harly said.

We didn't repaint and as Christmas approached I became more and more depressed. Almost every time I left the apartment I came back to find things disturbed and I had begun to watch constantly and carefully. When I left I would make certain everything was in order, drawers closed, shades drawn and so forth, and the moment I came back I would make a tour, looking for things that had been touched.

One day when I went to Kouberoff's office to pay my rent, he said, "I know who you are." Before I could answer I remembered the idiot character in a play who went around saying, "I seen you last night," and creating an absolute panic in people who were not certain that this was merely a device, and who had been indeed doing something censorious the night before. "I know who you are," he repeated, "an' I been watchin' you an' I been in your apartment an' I know everything you're doing." "And just what do you intend to do?" I asked. "I just know who you are, tha's all," he said.

I went upstairs to Bea's apartment and called the bank and put a stop payment on the check and then I called Harly. "Well, I'll be damned," Harly said. "I thought he was an s.o.b. but I never dreamed he'd do anything like this." "What shall I do?" I asked. "Oh, you'll have to move out," Harly said. "Tell him to go to hell and move right out."

Chapter 11

WHEN BUSINESS RAN SMOOTHLY it was possible to "turn tricks" as automatically and as thoughtlessly as a mail sorter might drop letters in the proper slots. One man could, from the call girl's point of view, look exactly like another; the act could be simply dull and repetitive and not even "register" enough to be repulsive or annoying. It wasn't sex; it was merely business. As Vivian, who had been a call girl for eighteen years, put it, "The first three times I thought I'd die. I memorized what the guy looked like and how he acted and I kept thinking, I'm having sex with a perfect stranger—I'm a prostitute— this is a perfect stranger and I'm in bed with him, and I almost lost my mind. Then the fourth one was just like the other three and the fifth one was like the others and after it hit fifty I didn't count any more, and after I'd been with two thousand it hadn't changed any."

Occasionally, however, the business would hit a snag—there were "difficult" Johns, insulting or disgusting ones, drunks and men who were inclined to be sadistic or violent. One of my Johns, a prominent real-estate man, was known to be a miserable experience. He saw a girl every week and the routine never varied. He would go to a hotel—a different one each time—take a suite and order a bottle of Scotch. After a half hour or so of drinking he would call for a girl, and by the time she arrived he would be droolingly, falling-down drunk. And once in bed he was impotent but optimistic, and the time would pass and he would have no intention of letting the girl leave. My first experience with him was a nightmare—after an hour I simply said I was leaving and he sat on me, tipped up the bottle and emptied it and said, "You *can't* leave. You just got here." "You are sitting on me," I said with some effort. "Get right up." "I'm sorry," he apologized sincerely and lay down on me. With a burst of energy I sat up, almost landing him on the floor, and he promptly tossed me back down and again sat on me. He was perfectly friendly about the whole thing but he couldn't see why I wanted to go home. It was another hour before I was able to get out and I was furious.

"You just have to know how to handle him," Marcia said when I told her. "He always acts that way. You just leave all your clothes in the bathroom and after about ten minutes in bed you excuse yourself for a minute, lock the door and dress, and then go tearing past him and out the door." "You collect in advance," she added. "He'll scream and curse you but he forgets it and the next time he'll be as friendly as ever."

The next week, in a different hotel, I tried it. I stacked all my clothes in the bathroom, laying them out for a quick change, and after about fifteen minutes of being pawed and rolled about I excused myself, locked the door, dived into my clothes, took a deep breath and unlocked the door and made a flying exit into the hotel corridor. To my horror, just as I rang for the elevator he appeared in the hall, stark naked, holding a nearly empty bottle and wailing, "But you just got here!" It was obvious that by the time an elevator came the operator would find him struggling to take me back to his suite. The staircase was next to the elevators and I started down that way and didn't stop until I had run down eight flights and was in the lobby. I looked behind me halfway across the room and to my profound relief there was no naked man with a bottle coming after me. "Oh, I forgot to tell you he'd run after you," Marcia said. "You did the right thing by taking the stairs."

Most of the regular customers were easy because they made a routine of sex, allotted a certain amount of time per week to it, did it in a set, routine manner and were completely predictable. Certainly the way the average John arranged his sex life would have little appeal for a woman. He preferred to come during the day, often in the early morning if it fit in with his business schedule. He didn't necessarily want to take off his shoes and socks or his undershirt and some kept their shirt and tie on. Most were only in the house for ten or fifteen minutes, which left little time for preliminaries—it was a brief, scheduled act. A few Johns liked to have a drink first, usually a quick shot of Scotch and a water chaser, if any. The conversation was limited to "Isn't it a hot, cold, damp, foggy or slippery day?" according to season, "My God you have a beautiful body," and "Well, I guess I'll be seeing you next week" (for sex seemed to be, for most men, a once-a-week act). In a few cases the regular customers would come in twice or three times a week. It was not expected that the call girl would fall in love with them, enjoy the act particularly, want to give them extra time or see them on a purely social basis. She was merely expected to greet them cheerfully, remember their names and small preferences (a pillow, no pillow, a drink or no drink, and if they liked an ice cube in their Scotch), appear to be going along with their brief passion, supply a towel and an interest in seeing them again. The relationship was simple and mutually satisfactory. Sometimes these Johns would show a folder of children's pictures, tell how bad business or their wife's temper was getting to be, and in turn there would be appropriate clucks of sympathy.

This emotionless attitude led many girls to feel that men were bestial, crude and base, as opposed to women's delicacy, love of romance and emphasis on the beauty rather than the relief in the sex act. I agreed but I always appreciated the Johns who were so businesslike in their attitudes; with them I could plan an organized day. The ones who "wanted the moon" were the bane of my existence. There were Johns who were hard to please and had innumerable fetishes and quirks that took time and ingenuity and infinite patience. A doctor who came weekly required a couple of hours. He was a nervous, apprehensive man who had to drink a great deal before he could relax, and he liked gin and tonic and asked intimate questions. He was a "leg man" and wanted the girl to parade around in black hose and fancy garters and shoes and nothing else; this sent the cleaning woman into convulsions when I would go out to the kitchen for ice. Since he tired of the same old garters I had to remember to buy new ones when I was in Bloomingdale's, and he liked the genuinely fancy ones with black feathers and tiny silver bells and red satin rosettes that looked like props from a dance-hall scene in a B movie. While I sat naked in my corny garters he remained completely dressed because the apartment was always chilly; in addition he had a dreadful habit of running his icy glass up my leg or back while he was talking. "I'd hate to have chosen him as a physician," I said once to Bea. "I imagine he keeps his instruments in a refrigerator, the damned old sadist."

Among the younger men there was a type known as "lovers," who were determined the girls would fall in love with them. Toward this end they would pinch and poke the poor call girls in a manner they thought would be exquisitely pleasurable to a woman. Since I'm sure they didn't all think of the same clumsy techniques, I am still looking for the marriage manual they all must have read which advises grabbing little handfuls of flesh and twisting, wringing of the neck while kissing, a stroking motion and patting on the flanks, similar to the way a farmer caresses a beloved cow, and spitting in the ears.

There has been a great deal said about the glamour of a call girl's evenings, and on the surface many of the dates were "glamorous." Thanks to expense accounts most Johns are willing to go to known supper clubs, order champagne and lavish food and go on rounds of clubs to see various floor shows; the average call girl, however, has one eye on her watch and will try to make the dinner as brief as possible, get back to the hotel and then home. And since a dinner date usually pays a hundred and involves about two and a half hours, and a nondinner date takes fifteen minutes and pays fifty, the night-club dates are only encouraged when girls are new in the business or, like Marcia, trying to get their names in society columns. Marcia and her ilk not only encouraged Johns to take them to the Stork and "21" but they haughtily refused to see most garment-district men on the grounds they were crude and the work was degrading. Bea, on the contrary, "went where the money was" and took me down to the wholesale fur center one evening to see five manufacturers.

At first glance it couldn't have been *more* glamorous. We went into a reception room that was filled with minked and sabled plaster manikins, and then through a room where rows of full-length fur coats, jackets, capes and stoles were hanging and then into a smaller room where garment men sat drinking Scotch and water from Dixie cups. At this point the glamour ceased and I began to see what Marcia had been driving at.

"Have a drink," one of the men said, slopping some whisky and a dash of tap water into a paper cup and handing it to me. The men on the couch moved over and I squeezed in and sat on the broken leather sofa; the springs had popped through and I balanced on several steel coils. The men had been in their shirt sleeves when we arrived and now one of them took off his shirt and trousers and hitched up his shorts. "I gotta be on the nine-thirty flight for Frisco," he said, "so let's get started." The man next to me got up and began undressing. "Are you Bea?" he asked me. "No," I said, "I'm Karen." "Well," he said, "let's go in the other room."

In the next room I found rows of furs, a tiny washbasin, a chair, and a naked light bulb dangling from the ceiling. He pulled off his clothes except for shoes and socks and eased himself down to the carpet. The huge windows were without shades or draperies and across the street I could see people working late in offices, some showrooms still open and models parading about with little circles of buyers watching. I had a feeling they were watching more than the models.

"Do you mind if I turn out the light?" I asked, since I couldn't think of anything to say about the lack of a bed. "Aw, hell," he said, "they can't see over here. I like it with a light on." While I pulled off my sable stole I tried to ignore the little plump man on the carpet. I hung my clothes on a hook, started to kick off my shoes and decided if he could insist on such casualness I would too and left them on.

I wonder, I thought as I joined him on the floor, if this carpet is made of burrs or if I'm just not accustomed to sitting on the floor. With great effort I looked directly at him. I usually ignored the way Johns looked, dressed or otherwise, but there was something about the bright, cold showroom and the rough carpet that brought the situation into sharp focus. He was a pudgy, short man with thin gray hair and scrawny legs. As he pulled me over to him I had a glimpse of several men in a window across the street—they were ostensibly arranging a display but I felt certain they were watching.

Before we were through one of the other men opened the door and came in. "You sure take your time," he remarked.

He was nude and carrying a bottle and some paper cups and he sat down on the carpet and fixed himself a drink. "You lovers coulda trown some furs down an' laid on 'em," he said, wiping his mouth with the back of his hand.

When the first John left we did just that—we pulled several full-length coats from the racks and "trew 'em down an' laid on 'em" and it was considerably more comfortable. It was fortunate we thought of this since all five men wanted to be with both Bea and me and we were there over an hour. When I was dressing in their little bathroom Bea came in and said, "Do you know we had to use that couch with the broken springs?" "How sad," I said; "we rustled up a bed of about fifty thousand dollars' worth of sable."

In a little over an hour we had each made two hundred and fifty dollars, and in a way that most call girls scorned. On the way home in the cab Bea said, "You know, in this business you give the customer what he wants. Men don't care if they do it in a bed or in a gravel pit and six minutes is their idea of a long time with a woman. Men don't want to neck and be romantic, and that's why they come to call girls. If you just do what *they* want, you save a lot of time and make more money."

Giving the customer what he wanted might be wise but it led to some complications. I had once gone to an air-conditioned motel on a broiling August afternoon and found the John sitting in a tubful of steaming water. "This is terrific," he said. I looked at his bright pink face and his lobster-red body floating in the hot water and said, "I'm sure it is." "You get in too," he offered, sliding over slightly. "I really don't think I'd enjoy it," I said. "You don't *know*," he protested. "I didn't think it sounded good till I tried it either." The argument ended with me submerged to my chin in hot water where I stayed for a solid fifteen minutes.

That time I went along with the customer. Other times I flatly refused. I refused to be covered with black shoe polish for one of Bea's Johns, despite his protests that it would come right off. I refused to wear a collar and leash and be led around an apartment and eat crackers from a dish on the floor, although I did consent to lead the John in that way, which partly satisfied him. I went along with the president of a local bank when he wanted to wear make-up (which I had to put on him) and high heels and an apron and be chased around the room and called Lulu, but I refused to tackle him and tie him to a chair and rape him, simply because it involved too much effort. I always said no to requests involving tying me to the bed, chairs or the sink and requests to have affairs with Johns' wives or poodles. When one of the ten wealthiest men in the world wanted to show me how far he could urinate I watched and applauded. When the same John wanted to scoop dirt from his window boxes and make mud messes, I mixed our drinks and helped him make mud and agreed that it was lots of fun.

Like most of the call girls I went along with mild eccentricities and drew the line at sadistic or masochistic plans. Almost all of us had been asked to participate in them and for sensible reasons it was a policy to say no. One girl had a John who lived on the twentieth floor of a Park Avenue apartment house whose idea of sex was suspending a girl by her ankles over the balcony rail. It only took a few seconds of this to satisfy him but he could rarely find anyone to accommodate him.

All in all I was considered very understanding about eccentricities. An actor who was then starring on Broadway used to come to my apartment late at night, dress in women's clothes (a fairly popular deviation) and go through a number of routines involving taking the clothes off and dancing for me. He was a past-middle-age dramatic star and by no stretch of the imagination a dancer and he often danced through several hulas and South American records. "I'd tell him to hurry up," Bea said when I explained that I was still in bed because he hadn't left until 3 A.M. "I'm sorry for him," I said. "He's so lonely and pitiful." "You get sympathetic with people like that and you'll be running a mission," Bea said.

Because of my apparent sympathy I was often sent "cases," as the really undesirable Johns were called. One was a sad little man who was rejected because he was difficult to get rid of and wore long underwear in three layers. Marcia neglected to warn me about him and, after we had been to bed, I made the mistake of offering him a cup of coffee. Six cups of coffee later he was still sitting in the kitchen, dressed in the several suits of underwear, which tucked into the high shoes he had also worn to bed. When Bea came home she said, "What's all this lint doing on the kitchen floor?" "It's from a man's long underwear," I said. "It seems to shed." "Oh, Ginny," she said, "didn't you know about him? Did he get in bed with his underwear and shoes?" "He sure did," I said. "I hope you told him not to come back," Bea said. "Of course not," I said. "I'm sorry for him. He's pitiful."

"Since you're so sympathetic," Bea said a few nights later, "I don't suppose you'll mind seeing a man I know." He was a well-known John in New York; he had a spinal disorder and was quite crippled and it was necessary to go to his home. There would have been no problem had he lived alone but he stayed with his mother. The mother herself would often place the call for a girl since the man had difficulty holding a phone, and she would answer the door and usher the girl into his bedroom. Afterward she would politely offer a cup of coffee and attempt to make casual conversation. The whole experience was rather ghastly and strained but he paid a hundred dollars and most of the call girls felt morally obliged to see the handicapped Johns and to be unusually kind to them.

If I could endure a surprising amount of humiliation for a handicapped person I found that I couldn't even be civil to drunks and the men from the rackets. The Johns who had to be drunk in order to see a call girl were the bane of my existence—I didn't know how to cope with them. The racket men, mostly from a New York branch of the inevitable Mafia, were impossible drunk or sober.

Alex was a drunk who was also a Mafia official and he was a regular John of Louise's. One below-zero night in the last part of January Louise called and asked me if I could send a girl over to the Waldorf. "Is it one of that Mafia crowd?" I asked. "Oh, hell no," she said, "they're all down in Florida." That sounded logical—if I were in the Mafia, which seemed to connote being in unlimited money, I'd have been in Florida. I sent Bebe, a rather pretty girl who was an alcoholic and excellent with Louise's Johns—she would often get drunk with them and spend the night gratis and have a fine time.

I sent her at nine thirty and at ten thirty she called and said, "I can't get out of here. I told him I couldn't spend the night because I had another date and he's thrown my clothes out the window." "Has he thrown *all* your clothes out?" I said, thinking that if it were only her coat she could get into a cab. "Even my shoes," she said. "I guess I'll come over," I said. I took an overnight case and packed a dress and shoes and carried an extra coat and went to the hotel.

When I got off the elevator on the seventeenth floor I saw Bebe standing, stark naked, pounding on the door of the suite. "That son of a bitch threw me out," she said furiously and resumed banging. "Stop making noise," I said. "People will come out and see you." "People already *have* come out and seen me," she retorted, giving the door a powerful kick.

"Here," I said, unzipping the suitcase. "Put this dress on and let's get out of here." A door down the hall opened and a small group of people came out. "Put it on *quick*," I said. Bebe didn't answer—she was staring at the people and they were staring at her. They went back in their room. "They'll call the house detective," I said. "Come *on*." I scooped up the suitcase and the dress and shoved the rather dazed Bebe through an Exit door. "We can't walk down seventeen flights," she said. "No," I said, "but we can get you dressed and go to another floor."

On the twelfth floor we rang for an elevator and when it arrived I recognized the house detective. Apparently he didn't recognize us for as we rode down he said to the elevator boy, "You didn't see no nude woman up there?" "Naw," the boy said. "If I'd seen a woman without no clothes, you betcha I'd still be up there." "I dunno," the detective said, "maybe them people just wished they'd seen a bare dame."

When we got home Bea said, "Some man's been calling from the Waldorf and he says he's paid a hundred dollars and if a girl doesn't come and spend the night he's going to float some people down the river." I called Louise and said, "Are all the Mafia people in Florida?" "Well," she said reluctantly, "maybe there's still one around." "And might that one be at the Waldorf?" I asked. "He might," she admitted.

The next time he called, which was in less than five minutes, I talked to him. He repeated his threat to float us all down the river. "I'm comin' over tomorrow night," he said, "an' if I don't get my money's worth there's gonna be some dead whores."

"You see," I said to Bea, "this is why I won't deal with that racket crowd. There's no reason to deal with the underworld any more than if we ran a restaurant—you can just work with businessmen and not get tied up in this." "You seem to be tied up in it now," Bea said. "What are you going to do when he comes tomorrow night?"

That was the problem. I worried about it until after midnight and finally I took a hundred dollars from under the mattress and went over to the Waldorf and knocked on his door. When he opened it he looked very small and homely in his satin pajamas and I handed him the money and said, "This will save you a trip tomorrow night and I don't want to ever do business with you again." Before he could answer

I shoved the bill in his hand and walked away. The next night I waited nervously but he didn't come. Louise called at eleven and said, "I just talked to Alex and he asked me to apologize to you. He thinks you're a fine woman and he'd like to bring some of his boys over Friday night and they'll pay whatever you want." "I just can't," I said. "I'm not going to live on pins and needles and anyway I wouldn't work with the Mafia at any price." Louise didn't insist. She had run a business almost exclusively for Mafia and Murder Incorporated and she had a collection of cigarette burns, knife scars and a facial tic for her efforts. She also had seven apartment buildings bought with her savings, but she could understand that some people couldn't sacrifice their peace of mind and possibly their lives to work the way she did.

When I took a firm stand about working with racket men, I assumed that I could run a safe business. All my Johns were honest people, and with most of them I had established actual friendships. I hadn't counted on the city detectives.

One morning I had a call from a man who said his name was Fred Tate and he wanted to come right over. "How did you get my number?" I asked. "Oh, I know lots of people you know," he said vaguely. "I gotta come right over," he added, "because I can only stay a couple of minutes. I just want . . ." I hung up on him. I was furious. Because of wire tapping none of my Johns would have announced what they wanted; for one thing it was hardly necessary. And when one of them gave out my number he always called first and gave me his friend's name and description. I called Louise, who seemed to have cornered the market on crude Johns, and asked her if she had given a Fred Tate my number. When I described the call she said, "Oh, honey, that was a bull. They've been on everybody's phone." "Well, they won't get in my house that way," I said. But I was worried. I knew now they had my number, and I could expect a shakedown of some kind.

The next day I had a call from a man who said he was Dick Brown, one of my regular Johns, but his voice sounded strange. 'I want to send a friend of mine over," he said. "His name's Henry." "Call me back in a few minutes," I said. I called Harly's office and, since he was in court, talked to Mr. Wallis, one of the partners. "Just tell him he's called a private home and not to bother you again," he advised. I did this and for several days I didn't have any faked calls, but then "Fred Tate" called and said that he was a friend of "Dick Brown's" and he and two friends wanted to come over that evening. I told him to check back in an hour and I called Mr. Wallis again. "Might as well get this over with," he said. "Tell him you and Bea'll meet them at the cocktail lounge in the hotel across the street and I'll go with you."

At eight that evening Bea and Mr. Wallis and I went into the lounge and joined three detectives. When we sat down one of them whispered to me, "Why did you girls bring your pimp along?" "He isn't our pimp," I said, "he's our lawyer. We want to know why we've been getting these phone calls."

"O.K., girls," one of the detectives said, "you made it this time, but stick around." We walked out, leaving them fuming.

"Be very careful," Harly said. "They'll be after you for some cash pretty soon." I *was* being careful. I was being so careful that I was frantic each time the phone rang. I checked and double-checked everything, and went down to the basement daily with a flashlight and checked the wiring for a tapping device and had a fancy lock put on the front door. And to add to my worries I thought I was pregnant.

I went to a doctor on Park Avenue and introduced myself as Mrs. Simon Blake and tried to make my hands stop trembling while he examined me. If I am pregnant, I thought, I'll have to have the baby. I was morally set against an abortion. What will I do with a baby? I thought. I can't even take proper care of a cat. I thought of all the call girls I knew who

ḥad children. Many of them had at least two, fathers un-
known, and sometimes the children stayed with their grand-
parents and many were in good, even fashionable, boarding
schools. A few of the girls kept their children at home. One
had a daughter nine years old and for that reason could never
"have company in" as it was euphemistically called, but had
to go to hotels or the John's apartment. She used a married
name and was rearing her child very properly with dancing
school and opera seats and riding lessons in Central Park.
On the other hand everyone knew another, a rather small-
time madam, who had her fourteen-year-old daughter home
from boarding school and working for her. The Johns said
the girl was so coarse she embarrassed them. I couldn't take
proper care of a baby, I thought desperately. I understand
older children but I wouldn't know how to pick up a baby.
I could remember having a friend hand me her infant while
she left the room and how terrified I had been. I had heard
they could literally jump like trouts and I held it very firmly
while it squalled, no doubt from the firmness of my grip. I
won't know what to do with it until it learns to talk, I
thought. How will I know what it wants until it can say
something?

The doctor finished the examination and said, with a fune-
real solemnity, "If you will dress I shall talk to you in my consultation room." I dressed with such haste that I left some
buttons undone and went into the consultation room zipping
my suit skirt.

"Have you and Mr. Blake tried to have children?" the doctor asked. Mr. Blake? I thought stupidly. Who the hell is Mr.
Blake? It was a full moment before I realized that the doctor
assumed if I were Mrs. Blake there must be a Mr. Blake.
"Well," I said slowly, "we haven't exactly *tried*, but . . ."
"Does Mr. Blake want children very much?" he asked. Oh,
dear God, I thought, I know that Mrs. Blake doesn't want
any. "I suppose so," I said, determined to take the news as a

young wife should receive such tidings. "I suppose he would be very pleased to have a baby." And poor Mrs. Blake, I thought, will be so pleased when she's out hustling in her eighth month to pay the hospital bill. "It is always very difficult for me to tell a young woman this," the doctor said sadly, "but I don't think you and Mr. Blake will be able to have a child just yet."

I must have appeared rather stunned for the doctor reached over and patted my hand and said, "If you will allow me to try a small operation . . . just a few days in the hospital . . . I think we may be able to correct it and you will have a child a year!" "That would be very nice," I said. "I'll ask Mr. Blake." I paid the bill and all but ran down the stairs.

"I'm not pregnant!" I announced joyfully to Bea. "I'm glad," Bea said; "I didn't feel up to a Havana flight." Most of the call girls went to Havana for their abortions since it was legal there and could be done in a hospital with a regular anesthetic. Since the revolution they continued to go but there had been some wild experiences with bearded soldiers invading the hotel rooms, and preventing the planes from taking off and so forth.

"Happiness is odd," I remarked to Bea that evening. "In this business not many delightful things happen to you but when something dreadful *doesn't* happen you can be hilarious about it." "I know what you mean," Bea said. "It's like pounding yourself on the head with a hammer. It feels so good when you stop."

Chapter 12

IT WAS THE WEEK before Christmas and now I wasn't simply discouraged, I was frantic. *What do you plan to do for Christmas?* Nell wrote, and I was sorely tempted to reply, *Sleep in Central Park,* which wasn't too exaggerated. Bea was no help; she had begun what Ronald called her Annual Toot, a Christmas drunk that ranged in mood from euphoria to the blackest suicidal depths; it was impossible to even talk seriously to her, although what Kouberoff knew about me he of course knew about her, and she was in as much danger from him.

Three days before Christmas Bea decided she hated New York; it was cold and unfriendly and she didn't feel needed. In Havana the revolution was in full swing and she thought Castro would appreciate her where Mayor Wagner probably did not; but this time she was drunk to saturation and completely irrational. I was staying with her and I had dozed off just after midnight, leaving her scrambling a dozen eggs with generous amounts of eggshell. At two, she woke me and announced she was going to Cuba.

"I don' give a goddam," she explained, "wha' *anybody* thinks. Ronald just wants me for my money, and you probably don' like me much, an' the cops don' like me. Anyway," she said after a pause, "Castro needs women an' I'm a woman."

She turned on the lights in our bedroom and began pulling clothes off hangers and piling them on top of me. "Where's a suitcase?" she said when I was all but buried. "Out in Jersey wi' dirty ole Ronald," she answered herself. "Don' matter," she continued, tossing shoes on the heap. She took down hatboxes and threw out the hats and stuffed dresses and shoes in. "Suppose the drug stores are open?" she asked me. "In Cuba, I mean."

"I don't know," I said. I was trying to think of some subtle way to call Ronald. "I'll take some make-up in case they're closed," she decided. She swooped a pile of perfume bottles and lipsticks from the dresser top into one of the hatboxes and tied the strings. "Dirty ole Ronald'll be plenty mad when he reads abou' me in Cuba," she said. "I might get killed with a bullet and I'll bet he'd be sorry." Apparently the idea appealed to her. "Suppose I'll be killed?" she asked cheerfully. She didn't wait for an answer. "Should I wear a hat on the plane?" she asked, picking up a big summer straw from the mess and trying it on. "It looks nice with your nightgown," I said. "Oh, I'll get dressed," she assured me.

An hour later Bea was still trying on outfits. "I don' know what the hell you wear to a rev'lution," she said finally. "You ever been in one?" By 3 A.M. she had decided on a black dress with a broken zipper and I had to get up to pin her in it. "I'm gonna get tickets now," she said efficiently. She sat down at the bedroom phone with a pencil and paper and got the number of Cubana Airline. "Do you wanna go?" she asked me. "I'll pay for it." I declined.

"Well," she said when she hung up, "they said they'll call me back in a half hour." She lay down on her bed in a tangle of hats and dresses and bedclothes. "Wake me up when they call," she said, and passed out.

I took the phone off the hook and turned out the lights but I couldn't sleep. I had been staying with Bea since I had canceled my rent check but I obviously couldn't go on living with her; for that matter I didn't want to live with anyone. I wasn't even so damn sure I wanted to live. The room was getting light and Bea was snoring and it was cold. Two clients were coming at ten and the maid was coming at ten and the kitchen was full of eggshell messes and the bedroom was full of a very drunk Bea Garfield. I was still worrying when I got to sleep and I dreamed about falling—falling from windows and falling from sand dunes and stepping into some sort of open construction. After each dream I woke up and after the fourth time around I got up and went in to clean the kitchen.

Eric Patterson, a kindly little old man who always came on Tuesdays and always brought a little gift, brought us a Christmas tree, a lovely, plump, long-needled tree with a stand that wouldn't fit correctly. When he left I tried to make it stand up and it would balance for a trembling second and pitch over; he had brought five boxes of bright, ugly ornaments, but it didn't help to wrap tissue paper around the tree's stem, and neither did cutting it shorter or making a point, and my heart wasn't in it anyway. The phone kept ringing and Bea woke up in the late afternoon and was furious because she didn't wake up in Havana and I gave up and laid the little tree in a corner and the maid finally took it home to cut into branches for her mantel.

The day before Christmas was very busy. A few men had to stay in the city and away from their families over Christmas, but most were simply having a final fling before spending Christmas week with wives, children home from school, and in-laws. One called me in the late afternoon and asked apologetically if I would have dinner with him. "I know it's Christmas and you'll want to be with your own," he said, "but if I could just be with you until seven thirty . . ."

He had come to me a year before, and it had been his first experience with a woman other than his wife. After twenty years of marriage, his wife, whom he described as a rather prim New England girl, had had an operation that affected the frontal lobe of her brain. When he went in to see her as she was coming out of the anesthetic, she was being hilariously obscene. He went out and demanded to see the surgeon, who told him it was a not unusual reaction to damage in this area of the brain and that they could simply hope the symptoms would be temporary. They were not and his wife was now cared for by a nurse in their home.

"I don't know what the hell to do," he told me at dinner. "Her mother's here for the holiday and the old woman just sits and cries and the nurse has to go home for her five-day vacation." I was in sympathy with him but it wasn't what I needed on Christmas Eve. I was relieved when dinner was over and I could escape.

"One of your Johns called you," Bea told me when I walked in the door. Bea's Christmas drunk was over and she was lying on the couch, pale and wan and sick as hell. "He wants you to come over to the St. Moritz." "On Christmas *Eve?*" I said. "What are you going to do?" Bea looked greenish. "Die, I think," she said weakly.

"Well," I said, "if I'm going to do that I'll have to change my clothes." I put my coat back on and went over to my apartment and found the key wouldn't work. I called Kouberoff and he informed me briefly he had changed my lock since I had stopped payment on his check, and he would see me in court. He slammed his phone down and I called Harly and said, "Merry Christmas and Kouberoff has locked me out." Harly said, "Merry Christmas to you too and we'll

sue him." "When?" I asked. "When I sober up," Harly said
and went back to his party.

I called Nell and wished her a Merry Christmas and she
said, "I feel so bad, it's Christmas Eve and there you are in
the big city and no date; I know there's not another girl
your age who doesn't have *some* sort of date on Christmas
Eve." "As a matter of fact, I do have a date," I said and hung
up and went to the St. Moritz.

"Do you want a drink?" I asked Bea when I got home.
"I don't drink any more," Bea said piously. "Well, I do," I
said, "and I bought a bottle of light rum and a bottle of dark
and I've forgotten how to make Jamaican punch but I'm sure
as hell going to drink." "Just mix them together," she suggested, "and dump some lime juice in it."

"How does it taste?" she asked after a few minutes. "Nasty,"
I said. "Let me taste it," Bea said, "and I'll see what's wrong."
I had simply poured both bottles in a bowl and added a bottle of ReaLime; she scooped a cupful and tasted it. "Vile,"
she said, taking the cup back to the living room. "Throw
some sugar in the bowl and bring it in here."

The living room was freezing and I brought blankets in
and we lay on the little modern couches and shivered. "Sugar
doesn't help it much," Bea said, taking another cupful. "You
know the joke about the man who sent the liquor in to be
analyzed and the report said 'Your horse has diabetes'? Well,
that's what this tastes like."

At midnight the chimes rang all over Manhattan and the
bachelors downstairs were playing "O Holy Night" on the
hi-fi with their doors open. "Did you call your mother?" Bea
asked rather suddenly. "I called her," I said, "and she wanted
to know if I had a date for Christmas Eve."

"*Mothers,*" Bea said. "You know, there was this girl used
to work for me—when she was a kid her mother used to
hustle in the back seat of a car and she sat in the front seat

and watched for cops." Bea scooped up another cupful. "She wasn't more than five years old," she added.

"I think that's the worst I ever heard of," I said. "Oh, the story gets worse than that," Bea said. "When she was six her mother told her she was taking her to see Santa Claus—it was Christmas—and she got her dressed up and dumped her at the orphanage and left her for eight years."

I took another cupful on *that* story. Downstairs they were playing "Silent Night" and after hearing Bea's tale Nell didn't seem too bad after all, and I missed her. At two we finished the bowl and I called Nell and told her I loved her. "Are you drunk?" she asked. "Yes," I said, "but I do love you." "Well, I love you too," Nell said. "After all," she added logically, "you *are* my child even if you are a mess."

The next night Bea went out to New Jersey to visit her children and left me alone in the apartment. "Don't you want to come along?" she asked me. "What will you do about dinner?" "Oh," I said, "I'll go out to dinner, or I'll have something sent in—I'll be all right."

The moment she left I regretted it. The temperature had dropped to the low fifties in the apartment. I was wrapped in an uncomfortable mess of clothes and fifteen minutes after she was gone I was hungry.

Two hours later I had eaten stale crackers and even more stale cheese, heated a can of imported turtle soup, tasted it and thrown it out, finished a bit of peanut butter and paced miles around the living room. I called four restaurants and was informed they didn't deliver on Christmas day, the implication clearly being that if I couldn't hustle up a dinner invitation on Christmas I must be beyond redemption. A liquor store was more understanding and for an extra fee they sent over a bottle of light and a bottle of dark rum and a bottle of lime.

By six the apartment was dark, the punch was gone and it was evident that even the Salvation Army wasn't going to take pity on me and deliver food and glad tidings. I decided to go to Chicago.

At seven I was on the plane and nearly had a change of heart; the plane was cold and almost empty and more cheerless than the apartment had been. As we started to taxi away a truck rushed up behind us, the driver and assistant tooting the horn and waving excitedly, and since I always assume that disaster is just around the corner I craned my neck to see if the wings of the plane were loose.

"Is anything wrong?" I asked the stewardess as she went past. "Oh," she said, "we almost forgot the salad." She sat down next to me during the take-off. "Everybody's been eating big dinners with their families," she explained cheerfully, "so we're just having cold cuts and gelatin."

Midway Airport was darker, colder and more wind-swept and deserted than LaGuardia.

"Don't you have no baggage?" the taxi driver asked me. "I'm not staying," I said. I gave him the address of my old apartment and sat back and tried to relax. The cab was very cold. "You're gettin' home late for Christmas," he said and I didn't answer. He tried again. "I been home all day," he yawned. "I been just sittin' on my fanny all day, seein' how much I could eat." I was tempted to comment "How gross" but a small inner voice said "Sour grapes" first.

"Just let me out on the corner," I said when we came to Maywood. There was a steady, strong wind off the lake and I wasn't any too well balanced in my high heels; I teetered along, staying close to the buildings and trying to avoid the uneven black ice, until I came to my old address and stood back and looked up at the windows.

The cranberry light was on at the second-floor landing and a huge Christmas tree filled the alcove in John's and Don's apartment; through the slanted blinds I could see Don doing something to the macaw's cage. In the background there appeared to be guests milling about. I thought of Okie, and the poor popeyed puppy that had been the miracle of a year before. Both humor and miracles seemed very remote. If I'd only known, I thought. If I'd only known how precious last Christmas really was—I looked up at the top floor and to my surprise there was a white Christmas tree with blue lights in our old apartment—I had fully expected the windows to be dark.

I walked over to the mailboxes and read *J. Miller and M. G. Bloch.* I stepped back again and tried to see someone in the top apartment but couldn't see past the tree. I wonder, I thought, if there are a couple of women in the apartment, or some of John's friends . . . and it occurred to me that I must look like one of the mangy little deer on cheap Christmas cards that stand knee-deep in snow and peek in at the family's Christmas cheer. I was mortified at my own analogy and miserably cold but I couldn't bring myself to leave. I had no idea why I was there, or just what I was looking for.

From under a parked car I heard a very faint mewing and I stooped down and tried to see where the cat was. I'd forgotten how many stray cats roamed around that neighborhood, and how it had worried me. The mewing seemed to come from behind me and I walked back and looked under another car and saw two very large eyes staring from a very small cat. I put out my hand and called kitty-kitty-kitty as I had done for so many years to catch frightened cats and stopped when I realized that if the poor cat came to me I couldn't do a thing for it. The wind whipped around the hem of my coat and blew a newpaper under the car and the cat dodged it and then crouched in another little tight circle. I straightened up and tried not to hear the mewing. Oh, goddam this world, I thought. Goddam all the sentiment and holiday spirit and the hypocrisy that lies behind thinking all's well with the world. I left simply because I couldn't stand to be near the cat and not give it help and anyway I had no reason to be looking in windows that no longer belonged to me.

The streets were empty both of traffic and people and I had to walk down to Michigan Avenue to catch another cab. As I walked past the uniformly multilighted windows I thought bitterly of how little control I really had of my own life—actually with all the work and planning and personal sacrifice I had put into my former life I had had no more control over my destiny than I had had in the airplane. In the taxi I rubbed my numb ankles and wallowed in self-pity. "Go to Midway via Hyde Park," I told the driver, determined to stick one more pin in myself.

When we passed in front of the family apartment I was gratified to notice that ours was the only undecorated window. They haven't got any more Christmas spirit than I have, I thought, and felt a little better. "Now go to Midway Airport," I said to the driver.

In the plane returning to New York I suffered from mixed emotions. I should have gone up to see them, I would think with a pang of remorse. Yeah, another thought would contradict that one, and explain why I don't have a date tonight, and why I'm twenty-six years old and not President of the United States yet, and why I'm wearing my hair this way. To hell with them.

At five thirty when I got back to Bea's I was so exhausted from lack of sleep and conflicting emotions and awful rum punch that I had trouble getting the key in the lock. My hands trembled and I fumbled around and twice I dropped the entire key ring. I fell into bed in my slip and at nine Marcia called and said, "I'm sorry to disturb you but do you remember Art Todd and his friend, well they're in town and can you get here in half an hour?"

Well, life does go on, I thought, looking in the mirror and trying to apply lipstick with a trembling hand. To my disgust I didn't appear to be a lily-white victim of deep sorrows: I had a nice, glowing pink color and my nose, possibly from the Chicago wind and more likely from the rum, was the glowingest pink of all.

"*My* but you look nice," Marcia said while I was taking off my coat. "You always look so healthy and happy, even early in the morning." "My strength is the strength of ten," I said, "because my heart is pure." Marcia took this with the seriousness she reserved for cultural matters. "Is that from Shakespeare?" she asked.

"Do you go in for sports?" Art asked me. "You always look so healthy." "I used to be a distance swimmer," I said. "Guess how much I weigh," he suggested. He pulled in his stomach and waited hopefully. "A hundred and sixty," Marcia guessed. "Guess again," Art said, getting rather purple from the breath holding. "More?" Marcia asked politely. "Two-fifteen," he said, letting his breath and stomach out. "I keep in shape at the gym," he explained. "*Look.*" After several false starts he stood on his head. "That's wonderful," Marcia said. The praise went to his head. For the next ten minutes we saw push-ups, sit-ups and wavering headstands. "If I had my gym equipment I could *really* show you something," he apologized.

I excused myself and went out to the kitchen for aspirins and when I returned he was demonstrating deep breathing. "Oh, *there* you are," he said happily. "Look, I'm gonna lay on the floor and there's something I want you to do." He lay down and flexed his muscles. "Now I'm gonna hold you by the waist an' hold you up in the air," he said. "I couldn't do that in a skirt," I protested. "I'll let you use my leotard," Marcia said in one of her rare streaks of malice.

While Marcia and Art's friend watched appreciatively I was held aloft by my waist, hung upside-down by my ankles and twirled about in a left-arm and right-leg hold. "Not bad for forty-five, huh?" Art panted.

"You're a good sport," Art said when he left. "That's what

I like about you, you're a good sport." "And you," I said to Marcia as the door closed, "are a dirty son of a bitch." "Oh, Ginny," she said seriously, "don't get mad about it. He's gone through that pitiful routine with me twenty times and he just needed a new victim." "I'm sorry to be unpleasant about it," I said, "but isn't it enough that I'm a harlot? Do I have to play straight man in their comedy acts too?" "Sure you do," Marcia said. "Three-quarters of them aren't nearly as interested in going to bed with you as in getting a listening ear. What do you think his wife would have said to him if he'd tried that act at home?" "Why," I said, "she'd have told him he was forty-five and to cut it out before he had a heart attack." "That's right," Marcia said, "and that's why he paid you a hundred dollars. His wife is only thirty and she's beautiful—I've seen her picture in the society columns—but men come to us for what they can't get at home and it's not always sex. It's usually appreciation."

"You've made me feel as useful and important as Florence Nightingale," I said. "And the next time he wants to play that game it's your turn."

At home I sat in a bathtub full of hot water and thought bitter thoughts. I'm not happy or healthy at all, I thought. I'm just so goddam well disciplined that I don't kick and scream when I'm miserable and let people know how I feel.

At six Bea came home and said, "Have you been sleeping all day?" "No," I said, "I've been out working. I've seen three people." "My *God,*" Bea said, "can't you relax at Christmas?" "I can't relax at any time," I said. "Well, you must want to amass a fortune," she said. "I don't even care about a fortune," I said. "I'm just accustomed to working."

When there was another call at midnight Bea said, "Get dressed in the cold and meet him if you must but you'll get pneumonia." "I'm just trained to keep appointments," I said, shivering into my clothes. "It's my New England-Scotch ancestry." "I think your Scotch forefathers would rest just as easily if you turned less tricks," Bea said sleepily. "They'd understand."

Just why *am* I doing this? I thought as I stood on the cold and windy corner of Park and Sixty-first and tried to hail a cab. I guess, I decided, that I've always been a compulsive worker. It was fine when I was doing useful work but I carry it over to this. I could have just seen Holt and made enough money but I felt obliged to work six nights a week if he needed me.

The next night Nicki, the Village girl who had helped me paint my apartment, went on a date with me to the Park-Sheraton. Our dates were with a convention and they led us through the living room of a suite filled with riotously drunk men and a few wives. Our dates, equally as drunk, steered us through without introductions and into the bedroom where they locked both doors. Just as I started to undress someone knocked and yelled, "Who th' hell's in there?" "Us," Nicki's date called back. "Go away."

Scarcely more than a minute later someone knocked on the other door. "Will you go away?" my date called to the unseen person. During the fifteen minutes we were in the room people pounded constantly on both doors and someone rattled the bathroom doorknob and was obviously peeking through the keyhole. *"My God,"* Nicki said while she put her hose on. "Your room is popular." *"Our* room?" her date said. He and my date laughed sheepishly. "Go on and tell her," my date urged. "Well," he said, "this isn't our room. We're on another floor—in fact, we don't even know whose room this is. We just figured everybody upstairs knows our wives, why not use one of the other convention rooms?"

"Yeah," my date said, "but now I'm kinda embarrassed to walk out of here." "You're embarrassed?" Nicki said. "I *won't* walk out." After much argument we simply pulled our coats up over our heads and made a run through the living room.

"You aren't mad at us?" the one with me asked when we were outside. "You know—we got to drinking, and our wives and all." "I'm not mad," I said. "It doesn't make any difference. It can't hurt my social rating." "I wish my wife were like you," he said wistfully.

"I didn't have a very pleasant evening myself," Bea said later. "Fred Lupino was here and he burned a hole in the mattress and while I was fixing that he burned a hole in the rug. There are a few compensations in this world," she added. "He gave me three hundred dollars to cover the mess."

Fred Lupino was consistently drunk, obnoxious and generous. He had been divorced by his wife, who had testified that he treated her cruelly, and he would arrive several times a month droolingly drunk, and want a girl he could go to bed with, call by his ex-wife's name, and weep and sob over. I had seen him once at "21" with a group of his business friends, clean-shaven, sober, and oozing charm. "Is that Fred Lupino?" I had whispered to Bea. "Sure," she said. "He just doesn't put on his company manners for us, but he's got 'em or he wouldn't be president of a company."

"He was awful tonight," Bea said wearily. "His ex-wife is getting married again and you should hear him weep and howl." "Doesn't he have any friends?" Nicki asked. "Not that he can cut up that way in front of," Bea said.

The next day Bea went to the beauty parlor and I was alone in the apartment. I wandered around and made tea and finally I just pulled a chair up to the window and sat and looked out at the row of gray buildings across the street. It was a cold, cheerless day and the streets were almost deserted. Gradually my thoughts went back, as they always did, to Griffin. A week before, Nell had forwarded two letters from Carol Rosenwald, one of my old students, and I had worried ever since about answering them. When I had Carol as a student she was a pawn in her parent's divorce case and wanted to run away from home with a goopy sixteen-year-old

boy from a local, public delinquent school; I had promised
to teach her to drive, her only passion in life, if she would
stay at home, and I had spent afternoon after afternoon
risking my neck and my car driving with a very nervous,
erratic Carol. When I heard that Carol had run away and
married another boy in the autumn, I decided my hours of
working with her had been wasted, but in her letters Carol
said, *The boy I married is not like Marty, he's very nice and
we have an apartment. I would have stayed at Griffin if
you'd come back but I didn't have anybody to talk to. We
all missed you so much. . . .*

When I read the letter I thought, Well, now I know that
in some ways I was appreciated there and it only makes it
worse. It's so much worse to know you've lost something important rather than just gone from one mess into another.

Harly called at six and took Bea and me out to dinner.
"We're taking Kouberoff to court next week," he informed
us, "and you had both better find new apartments before
then so you'll be well away from him."

In the morning we started out in the cold to look for new
apartments. "I know the plaster ain't good," one landlady
explained, "but come over here." At the front windows she
pointed to a small plot of dirt across the street. "It ain't often
you get to see green in this city," she said proudly, "an' in th'
spring they grows grass over there an' it's like havin' your own
front lawn."

"I'll be damned if I can stand any more of this city," Bea
said while we thawed out with tea in a restaurant. "I'm not
too enchanted with it myself," I said. "In Colorado," Bea
said, "Ronald and I had a house that was surrounded by
mountains on three sides, and we had seven kinds of trees on
our property." "Down at the cottage," I said, "it's completely
primitive—no electricity—just firelight and lamps and candles
—and there's the lake—and no telephone." Telephones had
become a sore point with me.

"If you love the lake so much, why don't you go back?" Bea asked me. "Why don't you go back to Colorado?" I asked her. "Well," she said, "sometimes I want to, but it seems you can never really go back." "That's the way I feel," I said. "I'm waiting for something—or, more truthfully, some-one—to come along. At least you can't go back alone."

Late in the afternoon we looked at an apartment in a new, tall, shiningly ugly apartment building; it had two bedrooms, an elegant kitchen with a dishwasher, and picture windows that looked out on smokestacks, a tiny patch of the Brooklyn Bridge in the far distance, and the wash from the tenements across the street. The rental was $350 and we took it.

"Do you like it?" Bea asked me in the cab going home. "No," I said, "I think it's hideous."

We moved on a Thursday and on Friday we went to court. I was tired from moving and I wore an old tweed suit from my Griffin days and the hallways of the courthouse were unexpectedly filled with newsmen. "I thought there weren't going to be any here?" Bea said to Harly after her picture had been taken repeatedly. "Well, guess who called them," Harly said. Kouberoff and his attorney had been pacing up and down the corridors, shuffling mysterious stacks of papers and talking to several tenants of the building who had come with them, presumably as witnesses against us.

Kouberoff took the stand first and he proudly explained how he had recognized me and, knowing who I was, set out to see how much evidence he could gather against me.

"First, I go in her apartment," he said, "an' I look in every-thing. I take papers outa de wasebasket an' I save em, an' I go through everythin'." Judge Wahl, a humorous civil-court judge who was presiding, addressed him directly. "Do you always enter your tenants apartments?" he asked.

"Sure," Kouberoff said. "I gotta right to know everything goes on in my building. I *own*.

"An' den," he continued to Harly, "I got in de mailbox, an' I take stuff out an' I save it." He pointed to the stack of papers on his attorney's lap and I recognized several of Nell's letters. "Den I fix blinds so I can look in, an' see everything goes on *all* the time."

"How much time did you spend looking in her windows?" Judge Wahl asked him. "Oh, as much time as I could," Kouberoff said. "I'm busy man, but I spen' four-five hours a day, look in her windows. I see everything."

"I'm certain you did," Judge Wahl commented mildly.

"An' I listen in de door," Kouberoff said. "All the time when I can, I listen in de door.

"I see her go to bed with men, and I watch that," Kouberoff went on. "Den I get down in da bushes, an' I look up between da blinds an' I listen an' I hear da man say 'I giff hundra dollars.' "

"Did you, now?" Judge Wahl said. "Go on."

"Den I see da hundra dollars, an' I tak a picture but it no turn out." "I told you it would be like a Keystone comedy," Harly whispered to me. I had been terrified the night before and tried to talk Harly out of going to court but he'd insisted that Kouberoff would get the worst of it.

Now Kouberoff, paying no attention to his own counsel's efforts to get his attention, told more and more, with Judge Wahl encouraging his testimony. Kouberoff described intricate plans he had made to trap me, get pictures of women going in and out and of men and so forth. The witnesses he brought were to testify that there was no hot water—the assumption being, I suppose, that inmates of whorehouses shower their sins away constantly—and that a guest of Bea's had once rung the wrong doorbell and awakened a woman on the third floor.

At the end of the session Judge Wahl delivered a scathing lecture to the very surprised Mr. Kouberoff, decided in our favor, and said he would pass down his full decision during the next week.

"Now aren't you glad we did it?" Harly said in the car. "We'll get a few thousand from him anyway. See how justice prevails?" "No," I said, "and I don't think we've heard the last of Kouberoff."

"You're getting to be a pessimist," Bea said. "Well," I said, "you said I was getting to be a paranoid when I knew he was looking in my window. I just feel this is going to be a mess; he won't cough up any money and you know it." "Nonsense," Harly said. "Nothing else he can do."

That night Bea had a champagne party to celebrate our court victory and the new apartment. Later, after we had gone to bed, Bea asked, "Are you asleep?" "No," I said, "I'm listening to those cats in the alley and worrying about them. Why?" "Oh," Bea said, "it's just what you were saying about always thinking the next day would be better. Don't you feel that way any more?"

"Let's think about tomorrow," I said. "What are we doing tomorrow?"

"Well, Bill Henley's coming over at ten," Bea said. "And tomorrow night we're having dinner with Jules, and before that we've got to get to the beauty parlor." "Does that sound any better?" I asked. "We might meet someone and fall madly in love," Bea giggled. "I think that's what we both need." "I need something," I admitted. "One day's so much like the next I have to keep looking at the calendar to see what month it is."

Chapter 13

AFTER CHRISTMAS the "season" picked up, and we were busy from morning until late at night and we never had enough girls. "Don't you know some that we could call?" I asked Bea one night after we had juggled appointments around to make seven girls cover where twenty could have been used. "I know plenty of girls," Bea said, "but most of them are on something."

I'd had an experience with the girls who were "on something" while Bea was away. A John had called and asked for Diane and I had simply looked her up in Bea's address book, called her and arranged for them to meet at my place. Just before the John arrived, Diane, a redhead with arms as thin as pipe cleaners and deep, black circles under her eyes, all but sleepwalked in from a cab and went into a trance on the couch. Marcia saw the John and then she and I maneuvered Diane into a cab and sent her home. "You should have asked me before you called her," Marcia said. "Well, her name was in Bea's book," I retorted. "Sure," Marcia said, "and when

198

she's not on the stuff she's a good hustler, but you can't use her when she's on." Now it seemed that almost half the names Bea had were unusable for that reason.

In the last part of January Edward R. Murrow began his broadcasts and the "exposé" attitude threw many call girls into fits of the jitters. "I'm going to go down to Florida," Marcia said. "I've seen these things before—they get a cleanup drive started and you never know where the ax will fall." "You're insane," Bea said. The next day the papers carried a story about a raid on a well-known hustling bar, with pictures of the two prostitutes who were caught. "I told you," Marcia said on the phone. "I told you it would start."

"That's a different case," Bea said to me. "Those bars that have girls are run by a syndicate, and those raids are a put-up job. A couple of girls are chosen as patsys and they pay them to do it. You'll see—those girls will be found not guilty. With what the racket guys pay off, the police aren't going to stage anything but a mock raid."

When the girls were released, Marcia said, "Well, they did get out of it but we don't pay off, and if anyone really has to go it'll be us." "Do you think we should arrange to pay off?" I asked Bea. "No," she said. "It isn't that sure. If you pay off to the politicians the only assurance you get is notice before a raid, and if they want you out of town they just give notice and then set their friends up. You can't deal with crooks and come out ahead." "Well," Marcia said, "I'm going to Florida for a month, and if this Murrow stuff cools off I'll come back sooner."

One madam, Lou, had her telephone "temporarily disconnected" the day Marcia went South. "I don't care," Lou said. "If I get busted it'll cost me five thousand apiece in pay-offs to get my girls out. It's cheaper to take a vacation and save the headaches."

"What about the madam Murrow described who put out a catalogue every year?" I asked her. "Do you know who she is?" "Yes," Lou said. "She's part of that man's imagination. He's been reading about the days even before Polly when there were *whorehouses*. Today whoring's a private enterprise, and three-quarters of the office girls and garment-district models and night-club girls are in it one way or another and it's such common stuff there's no room for big, fancy places."

"Murrow may have the wrong information," I said to Bea, "but he's stirring up a lot of suds. Don't you think we might go to Florida ourselves?" "We'll think it over," Bea said. There had been another bar raid reported in the newspapers, and things were even more tense. "We'll think it over," she said, "and maybe we can exchange twenty Johns with some of the kids down there and work in Florida for a couple of weeks."

That night we were raided.

On the sixth of February I awoke in a very small jail cell. It was early morning and still dark but I could see Bea sitting on the end of my bunk; she had a tiny mirror propped between the bars and was putting on lipstick. Bea was dressed in black and looked normal enough but I seemed to be wearing an odd outfit—slacks and a mink stole. My shoes definitely didn't belong to me. I had a terrific hangover and blurred recollections.

"You'd better put some of this lipstick on," Bea said. "I think I hear Harly out there."

I could vaguely remember calling Harly from the police station; I tried to remember why. Now I could hear him talking to the matron as they came down the corridor, and the scent of men's cologne preceded him. He looked perfectly wonderful and man-about-town; he was carrying a stack of newspapers and he spread one on the bunk before he sat down, to protect his cashmere coat. I have never hated anyone so much for simply being groomed.

"Here're your papers," he said, handing me the whole stack. "Look at the *News* first—it's the good one."

I was on the front page of the *News:* The picture showed my feet up on the station-house desk and I was smiling joyfully. The headline said V-DOLL IN AGAIN. I closed the papers.

"Don't stop now," Harly said. "Look at the *Post*. Look at the *Journal*. Look at the quotation you gave the *Journal* about suing the city. How drunk *were* you?"

"She was drunk enough," Bea said. "Look at the outfit she insisted on wearing. She said we might as well dress the part."

Harly gave me his comb. "Fix your hair before the photographers get hold of you again." I tried to comb it. "Now," he said finally, "we have about a half hour before the hearing. Tell me anything you can remember."

Bea did most of the telling. We had been raided a little after midnight. She was in the kitchen with Robert Eveleigh, Gail was in the bathtub, Barbara and Harry Evons were in the living room and I was asleep in the bedroom. There were about eight detectives and Deputy Commissioner Kennedy. When one of the detectives woke me he tried to make me put some clothes on because the Commissioner was there; that part I could remember. I had been sleeping nude and my first thought was that I had every constitutional, drunken right to stay nude in my own home. "Jesus, lady," the cop said. "I don't care, but the Commissioner's out there." "He's seen nekkid women before," one of the other detectives said. "Hey Joe—you remember when . . . ?" They both roared. I went out in the living room undressed but there was enough confusion so that even the Commissioner ignored it.

The detectives were trying to get a statement from Robert and he was drunk and telling them about his days as a major in the British army. His accent was still very strong.

"Are you for real?" a detective asked him. Robert blew up. He was livid. This mess, he shouted, was all Ronald

Garfield's fault. Ronald was a goddam pimp. If it weren't
for pimps like Ronald there wouldn't be whorehouses like
these. Not that, he added, this was a whorehouse. The cops
gave up on him for a while and began mixing drinks. One
of them picked up a bottle of Scotch and took me into the
bedroom. The "boss" wanted a statement from me against
Ronald. They were impressed by what Robert was saying.
I tried to tell them that Robert was Bea's ex-boy friend and
he had simply never forgiven her ex-husband for pawning
a six-thousand-dollar mink Christmas gift for five hundred
and then losing the pawn ticket. They wouldn't believe that
Robert was a friend and not a John. I got his framed picture
from the other bedroom. They were disinterested.

"Old buzzard's got a skinny neck, don't he?" one remarked,
looking at the photograph.

The "questioning" went on for several hours. Harry Evons
refused to talk at all; he simply covered himself up on a bed
and went to sleep. When the liquor was gone one of the cops
woke him up. They told me unless I wanted to press my
constitutional rights further and go "nekkid" on the street
I'd better get dressed. The officer who was sent to guard me
lest I escape told me I could take my time dressing.

We made an imposing exit from the building. They had
ripped our three colored phones from the wall and carried
them out for evidence; as we passed the doorman—eight men,
four women and three phones with twenty-foot cords dragging—one of the cops yelled, "Hey! Look at me, Maw! I gotta
tail!"

When we got to the station the press had already been
notified and were there with cameras. Bea put on dark glasses,
Barbara and Gail pulled their coats over their heads and I
smiled. I have crooked teeth and I've never smiled in a picture. I smiled and showed my back molars. I put my feet on
the desk and made quotable remarks. I was drunk and I

was in the right and I'd be damned if I'd hide my face. And every paper in town got a silly picture of it.

When the newsmen were through we were booked and taken in a paddy wagon to a women's lockup for the rest of the night. There the matron removed (euphemism for stole) everything in our purses but cigarettes, money and lipstick and we were put in cells—Barbara and Gail in one, Bea and I in another. Several women were there before us, and to my surprise I knew one of them. She was huddled in a Black Diamond mink and very drunk, having been brought in a few hours earlier on an assault charge. It seems her bathroom faucet had been leaking for a week and she refused to pay the rent until a plumber came. Her building manager refused to fix the faucet until she paid the bill. That evening she had been sitting there, drinking and listening to the dripping, when she had an idea. She demanded that the manager come upstairs. "Have you," Peggy asked, "ever heard of the Chinese slow-torture method with water drips?" "Have you," said the manager, "ever heard of paying your bills?"

Peggy was still drunk and very certain she had done the right thing when she knocked him flat. "If I had it to do over," she said, "I'd still do it."

I agreed. I told her how I'd stood up for my rights by going "nekkid." We agreed that we had both been very clever.

By the time Harly arrived I was feeling more sober and considerably less clever. "There's a real good shot of you in the *Mirror*," Harly said. "You look fine with your clothes unbuttoned. Did you really have two fifths of Scotch like you told the reporter?"

"You know damn well I don't drink Scotch," I said. "Do you think we can get out of this?"

"You'll get out of it," Harly said. "They haven't got a case—they have wire taps but they can't be used in court and they can't convict unless Harry and Robert testify against you."

That seemed reasonable enough. We were taken to the hearing in another paddy wagon, pleaded not guilty, the date for a trial was set and we went out on bail.

The morning of the trial I had a full mailbox. The Puritan Tract Society had sent me two pamphlets. One pictured a woman with a babe in her arms and a cigarette a-dangle from her lips. A devil's face was lurking in the curling smoke and a long poem described what nicotine would do to my immortal soul and also my milk.

The other pamphlet showed a red-nosed, puffy-faced man holding up a bottle and leaning on a public bar. *You may think it's fun now,* ran the caption, and on the inside was a list of *inescapable results of drink.* Among the inevitabilities were *a shuffling gait, trembling hands, brown tongue; soon the victim will have dirty, careless clothes, a broken home, a besmirched name.* . . .

There was a note from Nell. *I have never,* she wrote, *been so ashamed in* all my life. *And where did you get a* rabbit-skin *stole?*

I tried to remember. It seemed that at the station a reporter had asked me if my fur was mink or sable. I had jokingly said "rabbit." The Chicago papers had picked up the story and simply reported I was wearing a rabbit wrap.

Nonnie had typed a long letter. Never in *her* life had she been so ashamed. At least she hoped that *her* name could be kept out of it. However, in case I were committed to a mental institution, she would be willing to come to the town. When they let me loose I could stay with her. She hoped it would be the Menninger Clinic as the climate there was not unpleasant.

A man in Albany offered to forgive me my past sins and marry me. He had noticed in the papers that I sometimes made a thousand dollars a night; I must have a good bit saved and we could go into a decent business, buy a decent home and have a decent life.

I tore up my proposal and the letters from home. I put the pamphlets in my purse for Harly; it seemed we might as well find something to laugh about.

The trial began at one thirty. At twelve we met at a little tavern across from the Women's Court building. In addition to Harly we had Shelly Kravitz, another personal friend, and a separate attorney Barbara had hired. Photographers and reporters from the city papers sat around us while we discussed the case with our counsels. They all assured us the case would be dismissed that afternoon: Robert and Harry were both coming in to testify for us, we would not take the stand but simply continue our plea of Not Guilty. The case would have to be thrown out for lack of evidence. A newsman bought me a final drink and wished me luck. "You'll get out of it," he said. "The papers will be behind you." In his article the following day he described me as "in her cups . . . defiant . . . sure of acquittal."

It was snowing when we went over to the court; I put Harly's muffler over my head, took his arm and ran. I had forgotten how it felt to run in the snow—for that brief moment I felt rather giddy.

In the courtroom we were seated in a row facing the bench. The room was filled with reporters and lawyers from other courts; a tiny East Indian woman pulled up a chair behind me, adjusted her sari and took out a notebook. She was a feature journalist from Bombay.

The prosecution opened by putting one of the arresting officers on the stand; he was nervous and stammering, with an Oklahoma accent. He testified that he had spent three days in our basement, listening to telephone conversations and taking notes. How had it been done? Walll . . . he jest got him a box . . . and he sat on it . . . and he got him a board to write on . . . and away he went! The press snickered. Judge

Bushel laughed loudly. I signaled to Harly and whispered to him. He whispered back, What the hell did you expect? At this point I began to expect very little.

Then the impossible happened. The officer announced he would read from his notes, made while sitting on that box. Again I signaled Harly. Hadn't he said the notes couldn't be used? Well . . . it seemed they could be *used*, but not to convict us. They would simply establish reason for the raid. Harly went back to his position in front of the witness stand and the wire-tap reading started.

The first call was from Bea to Ronald. She asked him if he were coming in town. He said yes. He was bringing the children to the dentist. Bea said not to take Little Ronald out if he still had a cold. Ronald said O.K. Bea said to stop at Rosen Cleaners and get her tan dress. . . . At this point Harly objected to the call as irrelevant and Bushel agreed. It was stricken from the record.

The next call was from Marcie, Ronald's new wife, to Bea. Marcie had been furious with Ronald for taking a girl to the "21" the night before. This was followed by a long discussion of Ronald in the hay. Harly objected: The conversation was irrelevant. Bushel disagreed—he wanted to hear it. We heard it. The officer's face grew purple. The woman from Bombay wrote furiously. Bushel leaned over and listened.

The calls dragged on. One was from Ronald's uncle in New Jersey, who had called to ask Bea to come out there for Sunday dinner. The conversation was long and Harly asked it dropped as irrelevant. The court held that since "Uncle Al" was obviously a code name for a customer the call could be used as evidence.

A little after four thirty the trial was adjourned till the next afternoon. We went to a little Chinese restaurant far away from the court and the reporters. Over egg rolls our attorneys assured us that things were going according to plan. . . . The case would be dismissed the following day.

(The next day's gossip columns reported that we had all been drunk in a chop-suey joint.)

I went back to the apartment and asked the doorman to let me in (all our keys were taken in the raid). The apartment had been ransacked sometime during the afternoon. Clothes from the closets and dressers were piled on the twin beds, and all the unopened bottles of French perfume were missing. I couldn't have cared less—I simply pushed the debris on the floor and crawled into bed. I wanted to call home but of course the phones were gone. The liquor was gone. As tired as I was I hesitated to go to sleep: I wasn't sure who had my keys and I wondered if they would dare come in at night. I finally passed out from exhaustion.

The trial resumed at one thirty the next afternoon. The papers had published the wire taps and now the public came to have a look at me. As usual I was mistaken for Bea Garfield. "Look at that coarse face!" a woman commented as I went into the Women's Court building. "She just *looks* like a woman who'd sell other women's bodies!"

The same officer took the stand. The first conversation was between Bea and an "unidentified male." Bea whispered to me that it had been the ex-husband of one of the girls; there had been some alimony problem and he was trying to reach her. Bea had explained that she was at Bloomingdale's and would be back in an hour. The officer had added a touch of his own. Would the unidentified male like to see Karen? Sure he would, and he'd be right over. And Karen, the officer explained, was a name that I used. The court accepted this and it went into the record.

At three Harry Evons was sworn in. The prosecution asked him the standard questions: Had he come for purposes of prostitution? He had not. Was there any sexual activity planned or acted? No. Was any money asked? No. Or given? No. What was his purpose in being there, then? He was a friend of Bea Garfield's. Judge Bushel stopped the questioning and addressed Harry directly. Did he realize how serious this was? Of course. Did he *realize* he didn't have to testify for us in this way? That he could simply refuse to answer? Harry explained that he understood but he wanted to testify. He was dismissed.

It was announced that while Robert Eveleigh had been in court the previous day, he was on a business trip and not at this session. It was after four; could court be adjourned and Robert called for the next afternoon? Bushel denied the request. The prosecution rested. Since we had been instructed not to testify, the defense rested.

I sat with Harly in the outer room. Shelly and Barbara's counsel talked to some lawyers from another court. They all agreed that there had been no convicting testimony. We were called back into the court.

Barbara and Gail were dismissed for lack of evidence. Bea and I were found guilty; Bushel ordered us held for two weeks' investigation and then returned for sentencing. The matron was called from the back. "Don't worry," Harly said as she led us to be fingerprinted, "even if he gives you three years I'll get you right out on appeal bond."

Before we could be sent over to jail there was a long "health-department" procedure. In the courthouse basement we were stripped and given blue wrappers; a blood test was taken before the internal examination. After the tests we were led into another room for a penicillin shot.

On our way to the House of Detention the photographers followed the wagon to get last-minute pictures. Once there we were given an identical internal examination. "I just had a pelvic," Bea complained to a guard. "I know," the guard whispered. "But the doctor over *here* didn't get to look at you. She's got to earn her living some way."

Since we were not yet sentenced we could wear our own clothes. Only our shoes were taken—the metal tips could be used as a weapon—and we were taken to a shoe barrel in a

back room. It took a while to find shoes since most were one-
of-a-kind; Bea found two size-nine saddle shoes without laces
and I had brown Oxfords with Cuban heels, also without
laces. "We throw all the laces away," the guard explained.
"You might hang yourself." "You know," Bea said, "I just
might."

We were assigned to the fourth-floor dormitory, given
gray blankets, even grayer sheets and left to our own devices.
The dormitory was simply one big, brightly lighted room
with fifteen beds, fifteen women, a few chairs and two tables.
At one table the Puerto Ricans sat together, chattering like
monkeys; a very young girl was crying and an older, very
wrinkled Spanish woman was whispering to her.

"That's a mother and daughter," Ruth, the girl in the next
bed, explained. "They're off up here." She tapped her head
significantly. Ruth didn't look too bright herself; completely
toothless, she had big blank eyes and walked with the char-
acteristic shuffle of the simple. On the other hand the Spanish
couple looked worse. They were both cross-eyed and very
hunched; the daughter's hair hung over her face. "They take
stuff," Ruth said. She made hypodermic-shooting gestures.
"They don't even speak no English." Ruth was over on my
bed by this time, whispering confidentially to me. "When
they brought 'em in they was hollerin' and kickin'." Ruth
flayed the air with her skinny arms and legs to show me how
they had fought the guards. "I been here ten times," she
added. "I don't care when they bring *me* in. Are you the
schoolteacher?" she asked abruptly. I admitted it. She had
been hoping I'd come in; she had a project that needed help.
The bar on Forty-third where she worked catered to sailors,
and most of them had said they wanted to marry her. She
figured that while she had spare time she'd write to maybe
ten of them and accept those proposals; she could ask each
for fifty dollars for a divorce. Then she'd take all the money
and buy new teeth. With teeth she could get a rich husband

and not have to bother with sailors; the problem was to convince them she really needed a divorce before she could marry.

An older woman with a severe twitch came over and joined us on the bed. "I should know all about the *navy*," she began in a carefully refined voice. "My husband was a rear admiral in the navy until the day of his death." "I heard that before," Ruth said bluntly. The woman took no offense; she didn't seem to hear the insult. She poked at her falling hairdo with trembling fingers. "He was from one of the very finest families in the South," she continued. "You won't think that story's so damn interesting the tenth time you hear it!" a colored girl called over to me.

I didn't think it was so interesting the first time. I just couldn't escape.

The evening dragged on. The colored girls played poker; Ruth began composing her letters; the Southern woman cornered the Spanish woman's simple daughter, who couldn't understand a word of English, and told her about the home she and her late husband, the rear admiral, had owned in Roanoke. Bea and I tried to make up our beds. Since the straw-filled mattresses were covered with slick rubber and the sheets were merely narrow strips, there was no hope. "This reminds me," I said to Bea, "of that time I got the bridal suite at the St. Moritz. Remember those satin sheets?" "In no way," Bea said flatly, "does this remind me of a bridal suite."

At eight another wagonload came over from the court and three more came into the dormitory. One heavy-set colored girl was in for the twelfth time. Since almost everyone was an old-timer they knew her.

"How'd you get caught again?" Ruth asked her. She had picked up a Harlem detective. But she was surprisingly triumphant. "Bull, he comes up an' asks me if I want a good-time and fifteen dollars. I tell him, my old man gives me my

good-times and if he want me he can pay me twenny dollars.
He say awright and I take him to the Delmar.

"We git up in that room an' he says what I *give* him for
his twenny dollars. I said I ain't seen no twenny dollars yit.
He gives me the twenny dollars and then he pulls his badge.
He says, give him back that twenny dollars.

"I sticks it in my mouth. He say I gotta give his twenny
dollars. I say he can go to hell. He say, when we get ter th'
station, the sargeant *he* make me give the twenny. We git
down at th' station an' the sargeant, he say give the man dat
twenny dollars. I say I got that twenny stuck up where ain't
nobody gonna fin' it. Sargeant say when I gits ter th' jail, the
matron git it an' give it back. When I gits here the doctor
look, the matron look, nobody fin' it. That officer just *hoppin'* around."

Marlene showed a very crumpled "twenny dollars" in her
hand. Everyone roared. Even the Spanish-speaking knew
what twenty dollars meant.

We went to court to be sentenced on a Wednesday, after
fifteen days on the detention floor. "Do you suppose the photographers can get in there?" I asked Bea at 6 A.M. when we
were dressing to go in the police bus. We were both a strange
greenish-gray from worry and lack of sleep and lost weight,
and no amount of make-up seemed to help. "I hope they
can't," Bea said, "but do something with your hair anyway."
I tried to fluff my hair up but it was impossible. I finally
pulled it back and made a little hard twist and secured it
with black bobby pins. "Elegant," Bea said, "elegant."

We shared the mirror with Alice Gonzalez, a perfectly
beautiful, completely psychotic colored girl who had a disconcerting habit of pulling off her nightgown after lights out
and parading back and forth in the moonlight. Her figure
was lovely and some of the colored girls who knew her from
the streets said she'd been a stripper before she became
"screwy"; often her nude parading included bumps and

grinds and her nocturnal jaunts frequently stopped at some-one's bed. Despite her beauty even the most avid Lesbians rejected her—"She's too damn crazy fo' me," one said—and sometimes there would be a battle getting her back to her own cot. Alice had decided that since all men found her passionately desirable, she would vamp Judge Bushel and he would let her go. Her mother had been instructed to bring one of her "evening dresses" for her court date, and now, at 6 A.M., she was garbed in a filthy, torn, ankle-length blue-satin party dress and gold slippers.

"I theenk I shall wear my hair up," she said, affecting the Spanish accent that was part of her claim to being Cuban. She piled her long hair loosely and poked a few bobby pins in the swirls. "You look beautiful," she remarked to me without looking at me. "I pay three hundred dollars for theese dress," she continued, "an' my sleepers were given to me by a vary wealthy man." A howl of laughter went up from the girls who were lying on their cots, watching us get ready for court. "You tell us 'bout 'de rich man give you dat dress," Marie said. "I wanna hear 'bout dat man." "Let's use the bathroom mirror," Bea whispered to me. We'd heard fifteen days of this bickering and we'd had enough.

In the bathroom we tried to cover the circles under our eyes with make-up and found it a losing battle. "Put lots of mascara on," Bea said. "At least your eyelashes will be as dark as the circles." Rhoda, a fifty-five-year-old prostitute with unearthly white skin and flowing, crimson hair down to her waist, was sitting on one of the washbasins brushing her hair. "That jedge ain't gonna look at you," she said wearily. "I been in front of that bastard twenty-seven times and he don't know me yet." She stopped brushing her hair and began to braid it. "I'm going to get me thirty days this time," she said. "I got ninety days last time an' I'm gonna get me thirty days this time." She wound a rubber band around one braid and started on another; her hands were covered with gigantic, boil-like drug abscesses and swollen to three times their size and she used them painfully. "Them bastards kilt my dog," she said. I tried to hurry with my mascara—it was a story I didn't want to hear again. "They come right in my room an' when he started after them, they shot him an' he was nothing but a little bulldog puppy." I put the mascara in my purse and started out of the bathroom, leaving Rhoda braiding and weeping.

"I can't take that story," I said to Bea when we were sitting on our cots. "I can't take that woman," Bea said truthfully. "There's nothing I can do to help her, and I can't stand looking at those abscesses."

At seven thirty they came to the dormitory for the five of us who were going to Women's Court: Rhoda, who was wearing a dress nearly down to her ankles "to cover up my marks —I don' want that judge to know I'm no junkie"; Alice, who had added rouge and piles of rhinestone jewelry and had painted a "beauty mark" the size of a quarter on her cheek; Bea and I and Carrie, a three-hundred-pound black Negro woman who had stayed in her corner the entire two weeks, singing hymns and crying for the two-week-old baby she insisted had been taken from her when she was arrested and that we were assured by a reliable guard she never had in the first place.

At the court building we were all put in a large, bull-pen cell. Rhoda sat in a far corner of the bench and wept for her dog, Carrie sat on the opposite end and keened for the baby that had never been, Alice sashayed up and down, holding her dragging satin skirt before her in a regal manner and practicing dramatic speeches to be made in court, and Bea and I sat together and worried. "Do you suppose he'll give us three years?" Bea said. The newspapers had indicated that we could get a three-year sentence. "I suppose he could give us anything," I said.

At ten Rhoda came over and sat with us. "You know," she

said, "I never heard of call girls going to jail." "I never have either," Bea said. "I been coming to jail in this city for thirty-five years," Rhoda said, "an' I only remember 'bout three others comin' to jail. An' one of them used to go with the bastard that was mayor then, an' when she broke off with him and went with a racket guy, the very next day the police came and got her and she was in jail for six months." "Thank God we haven't been unfaithful to the mayor," Bea said.

At ten thirty we were all taken downstairs to the anteroom of the court, and Alice was the first case called. Over the protests of her Legal Aid lawyer, who pleaded with her to cover herself with her coat, Alice swept into the courtroom, her hair falling in her face, her ragged skirt billowing behind her, her rhinestones clanking. We managed to watch the proceedings through a crack in the door.

"You have a husband and infant," the judge said. "Would you like to go home to them?" "I would *not,*" Alice said grandly. "What for do I want to go home to my husband? He kicks me."

"You *do* have an infant," the judge said. "Would you like to resume the responsibility of your child?" "Nothing but a bastard," she dismissed her infant. The judge spoke for a moment to the Legal Aid attorney and the probation officer who stood at the bench and then addressed Alice. "Your husband is waiting for you," he said briefly. "I am giving you thirty days and suspending the sentence. Go home with your husband." Before Alice could protest, her attorney, a harassed-looking, bespectacled young man, grabbed her by the elbow, scooped up her coat and dragged her out of the court.

"He gave her thirty days las' time," Rhoda explained. "He didn't want to give her no more time."

Rhoda's case was next. She pulled her sleeves down to cover the abscesses on her hands, pulled her collar up to cover the deep abscess scars on her neck and walked into the court, her braids bobbing down her back.

Contrary to her belief that the judge didn't know her, the first remark he made was: "You here again?" Rhoda murmured something inaudible. She kept her eyes cast down and tugged at her sleeves. "Well, I'm pretty sick of you," the judge said. "Ninety days." Instantly she came to life. "I *can't* do ninety days, Judge!" she screamed, jumping up and down, her dirty gray skirt and her braids flying. "I can't, I can't, I can't! Can't do no ninety days!"

The judge looked up briefly. "Think you can do sixty days?" he said. "I *can't!*" she said. "I got clothes in my room, Judge, an' they'll take em off an' I just done ninety days an' I can't *do* no sixty days!" "Well, do you think you can do thirty days?" he said. "Oh yes, Judge," she said. "I sure can do thirty days, thank you, Judge." Grabbing up her skirts she dashed back to the anteroom. "Lord God," she said, flopping breathlessly in a chair, "I sure did have to work for that thirty days."

Carrie was next; the police matron led her into the court and she stood in front of the judge, her face in her hands, sobbing. "She pleaded Guilty, is that right?" the judge said to her attorney. Carrie said something and the judge turned sharply to her and said, "What did you say? Speak up, what did you say?"

She whispered something and her attorney said, "She says she wants her baby." The judge turned and consulted the probation officer. "She doesn't have a baby," he said. "The officer tells me they have checked and she has no baby." After a few minutes of whispered conference with the lawyer and the probation officer, Carrie was given sixty days, suspended sentence.

"Thank you, Judge, thank you," she said, putting on her hat. "I sho' do want to git to my baby." Her attorney rushed her out of the room and we were called.

"I could give you six months, which you deserve," Judge Bushel said to me, "but since you did not testify in your own behalf and perjure yourself, I shall give you three months."

When the sentence was pronounced I found that I was weak with relief; I had believed that we would be treated with special venom and I had expected worse. He gave Bea the same sentence and we were taken in the back to be finger-printed. "I wonder," Bea said, "if we had jumped up and down and wept if he would have shortened it like Rhoda's?" "I'm certain he would," I said, "and I'd gladly sit in the pokey the extra three months before I'd do that for him."

In the bus going back to jail Rhoda said, "I thought you kids would get three years for sure." "Why?" I said. "Well," she said, "they got it in for you or you wouldn't be here in the first place."

For the first night we were put on the eighth floor with the other new prisoners. Bea and I were given a cell at the back of a corridor; it was tiny and pitch-dark although it was only four o'clock, and the huge, straw-filled mattresses slopped over the narrow steel cots and touched, making it necessary to crawl or walk over the beds to get to the wash-basin at the opposite end. The sink was cracked and several large, black water bugs were crawling in a pool of water on the floor. "The cells on the other floors are much better," the guard said. "This is just where you stay the first night until we can classify you."

She left and an old woman promptly appeared and poked her head in our cell. "You got a worse one than I got," she said, looking at the overlapping mattresses and the water bugs. "I had this cell last time but I got a real nice one now." She crawled over the mattresses and sat. "You'll move tomor-row," she went on, "an' you'll have a real nice cell an' you can fix it up pretty."

"What are you in for?" Bea asked her. "Livin' on the ban-ner," she said. "And what's that?" Bea asked. "Oh, sleepin' in the park, just gettin' what you can get," she said. "You'll like it here, once you get your cell fixed up pretty."

At eight thirty a heavy colored guard came around and slammed the individual gates shut and turned out all the lights with a master switch. I lay down and moved as far from the wall as possible to avoid the bugs that were climbing. Unlike the dormitory, the cell was completely without light, either from the street or the corridor, and while I could hear the rustling as the mice came out, I couldn't see where they were. Lying in the dark, listening to the slight noises of the rodents and bugs, I felt overcome with despair. My life was completely out of my control. I felt tears starting and was immediately aware of the heavy mascara I had put on before court and what would happen if I cried. In the dark I groped for the washbasin and removed my make-up.

"What the hell are you doing?" Bea said as I scrambled over her. "I'm going to wash my face," I said. "I'm not going to wash until I get out of here," Bea said, "I'm going to go on a dirty strike."

With what must have been laundry soap I scrubbed off the mascara, rinsed in icy water and crawled back over Bea to my own cot. Once in my bed I found that the urge to have hysterics had passed.

"Are you asleep?" Bea said. "A cockroach just crawled over me." "No," I said, "in fact I'm not sleepy." "God," Bea said, slapping at something on her blanket, "I hope Harly gets us out on appeal. Think of all the things we'd be doing if we were out."

"I was just thinking of that," I said. "We'd have a house full of drunk Johns. At least we're in bed early." "Thank you, Pollyanna," Bea said. She turned over and pulled the blanket around her. "Don't sleep with your mouth open, Cheerful Cherub," she said. "You might swallow a cockroach."

Chapter 14

IN THE MORNING we were transferred to a cell on the ninth floor which was considerably better, having a window and small enough mattresses to allow a path through the room. We were also given a large stack of shower curtains. "And what are these?" Bea said, shaking one out. Milly, a middle-aged white streetwalker from the next cell, said, "Come over to my house and I'll show you." Bea winked at me about the "house" euphemism and we went next door.

Milly's cell resembled a small back yard on washday. She had shower curtains taped to the walls, hung on poles, draped over the cots and toilet and little steel table; two curtains, strung on a suspended hoop, surrounded the washbasin. "You decorate your house this way," she said. She pointed to cardboard, crayon-colored crucifixes pinned to the curtains, pink crepe-paper bows, bits of ribbon and colored material tacked around at random. "These here is contraband," she whispered, "an' they raid once in a while an' take it away because you ain't suppose to have it, but it's pretty while it lasts.

218

Now come on back to your house," she said briskly, "an' I'll help you decorate."

Bea looked horrified. "If you don't mind," she said with some embarrassment, "I'd rather not decorate."

"Not decorate?" Milly said. "Why, you can't live in an undecorated house. You *got* to fix your house up."

"I think you've just made an enemy," I said after Milly left in a huff. "I guess I have," Bea said, "but I couldn't stand having that crap hanging all over the cell." She folded the shower curtains and put them under her cot. "On second thought," she said, "maybe I'll hang one around the toilet. Privacy is nice."

While I was helping her hang our one "decoration" a guard came and announced we were to go down for "work classification."

"There isn't much work to do around here," she said cheerfully as we went down in the elevator, "but they'll find a little something."

Captain White called me in her office first. "I don't know just what you can do," she said. "Would you like to work in my office?" "I wouldn't like to work in any office," I said. "I can't type and I can't file." "I was trying to help," she said. "The only other work is scrubbing floors or working in the kitchen." "That would be fine," I said. "Just a moment," she said, and went into the office to make a call. "You'll work on the second floor," she said, coming back in. "The guard will take you there to meet Mrs. Archibald."

When I started to leave she said, "I'm sorry you don't want to work in my office."

"I'm scrubbing floors, too," Bea said when we were back in our "house," "but why didn't you work in her office?" "Because I don't want to think her thoughts," I said. "I can scrub floors and keep my mind to myself. In her office I'd have to think about her letters and her phone calls and listen to her talk about her work and her problems. They can't control my mind even if I do have to sit around here for three months. Anyway," I added truthfully, "the floor I scrub is just a little corridor about ten feet long; I don't think it'll be much effort."

At eight the next morning Bea went to dust the desks in two downstairs offices and sweep and I went to scrub my corridor. At eight thirty we were through and back in our cells.

"Captain White asked me how you were," Bea said. "I think she's insulted because you wouldn't work for her." "I like mopping," I said. "It's very satisfying work." My mopping partner had actually done most of it for me; Irma, a muscular light-skinned colored woman who was in on her seventh assault charge, had taken a liking to me.

"I wanna tell you somethin'," she had said confidentially, drawing me aside. "Dese bitches 'round here, dey'll do *anything* to you, if you let 'em. You gotta watch all de time." "I'll remember that," I said. "I ain't kiddin' you," she had continued. "Iffen you don't watch your pail and mop, wham! Dey'll go and put a hex on it fo' you and how you like *dat?*" "I'll watch my pail," I said. "Dat ain't all," she said. "Dis bitch in de streets, she puts a hex on me, a spell, an' she fix me so's I kaint breathe right. I goes to breathe an' "—she took a deep breath and demonstrated—"it *sticks* right here. I git holt a that bitch, I bust her head." She laughed. "Das why I'm here again," she added.

I kept a safe distance from Irma but she remained as friendly as a gigantic bear. "Never min' about dat flo'," she said. She gave her corridor a couple of vicious pokes and moved around to mine. "I finish it fo' you," she said, "but I use my own mop. I don' like de looks of yours. It got a mean face."

I took my mean-faced mop over to the side, sat down and let her work. In ten minutes she had all but wiped the pattern off the linoleum. "Dere," she said. "Now I gonna spit on my mop"—she spit—"an' jest let dem bitches put a hex on it now!" She carried it off to the broom closet and I slipped away to the elevator.

"Wait'll you see the babe I work with," Bea said. "She's supposed to be the hottest thing in Harlem—I think her cell's in the next corridor."

At lunch the Hottest Thing in Harlem sat at our table and Bea introduced us. Barbara was six feet tall, statuesque, and had a red wig with a long pony tail. "Come on over in my house after lunch," she said, "an' I'll try to fix that dress." I was well aware that my dress needed fixing; after our work interviews with Captain White, Bea and I had been taken to the Clothing Room to choose six dresses, a pair of shoes, a sweater and underwear. We had tried on several sizes and only succeeded in sending the girl who worked in Dresses into hysterics. "I never seed nothin' so funny in my *life*," she had gasped when Bea put on a size 16. "You better not take dat one."

The dresses, made in the sewing room by the inmates, reflected their antagonism clearly. A dress might have a full size-20 top and taper off to a size 10 on the bottom. Sleeves were put in backwards, collars sewed together making a chokingly small neckhole, and the seams were dizzily zig-zagged. All the dresses were cotton and of the Monkey Ward housedress gender, with patterns of pink rosebuds, tiny sprigs of blue forget-me-nots and so forth. The shoes were heavy oxfords and the underwear was handmade with as much malice as the dresses and we decided not even to try.

Coming back from the Clothing Room with our little piles of clothes, Bea said, "You know, except for the old women I don't see *anybody* in dresses like these." She was right—almost everyone wore solid-color dresses, made in straight sack-dress style, very tight, pegged at the bottom and stiff with starch. Our dresses were limp as dust rags.

"You come on in my house after lunch," Barbara said, "and I'll get your clothes fixed up."

In Barbara's cell there were stacks of solid-colored dresses, pins, needles, thread and, under the mattress, scissors. "You've just got to have connections," she said, pinning one to my size. "It's just like in the streets, you've got to have a connection. Now, it'll cost you a pack of cigarettes for each dress they make fit you down in the sewing room, and a pack every time you want one washed and starched."

"To hell with it," Bea said. She had chosen all her dresses in size 22, the largest they had, so they would be comfortable both top and bottom. "I'm just as comfortable without the starch." She folded the extra yards of pink rosebud material around her and sat down. "You can't go around like that," Barbara said. "You look like a perfect fool." "Couldn't care less," Bea said. "I wouldn't look any prettier in one of the starched ones. They look like blue chambermaid uniforms."

I had four dresses pinned up and we went back to our cell. Bea had a letter from Ronald, enclosing little carefully printed notes from each of her children, wishing her a happy trip and asking her to write about the places she was seeing and the fun we were having. I had two letters from Nell.

I am getting older [Nell wrote] and your grandmother is an old woman, and we are not well. I have asthma and wheeze constantly and your grandmother has one cold after another and your poor father goes to work every day.

We used to be so proud of you when you were a school-teacher. We never expected anything of you but decency and honesty and a respectable name. . . .

I tore the letter, all fifteen big pages of it, and all the enclosed newspaper clippings into shreds and threw them down the toilet. To my horror after they went down there was a deep gurgle and the water and letter slowly rose to the top and over.

I sat down and wrote a bitter letter to Nell and told her that I would thank her to let me enjoy my three months in jail without her advice or comments. *It's the first rest I've had in ten years,* I wrote, *and it's the first time I've been where you can't get in and bother me. When I look at these bars, I don't think that I can't get out. I just realize you can't get in and I'm eternally grateful to the City of New York.* After penning several more pages I sealed it and dropped it in the mail chute before I could change my mind.

The next morning Captain White called me to her office and said, "I don't believe I told you but I am on the censoring board and I just read the letter you wrote to your mother." I said, "I'm certain it was necessary for you to read it but I don't want to discuss it with you."

"I think you misunderstand me," Captain White said. "It's just that I have a daughter a little older than you are, and I haven't seen her for five years and she hates me as much as you hate your mother and I wish I could talk to you about being nicer to your mother." "I'm afraid you misunderstand *me*," I said. "I don't hate my mother at all, in fact I love her very dearly and I see her constantly. It's just that we are too close and see each other too much and we're both very neurotic and shouldn't be together all the time."

"Well, I'm sorry then," Captain White said. "You even look like my daughter and I haven't seen her for five years, and she says that I'm just what you'd expect a policewoman to be." "Are you certain she hates you?" I asked. "Yes," she said. "At least you write to your mother and she doesn't even write to me. All I know is that she's in Oregon."

"You know," I said to Bea after lunch, "I'd like to just have my own problems once in a while. Wouldn't you think the police would jail me and let it go without telling me their family secrets?" "You just look maternal," Bea said. "Well, I'm not going to mother a sixty-year-old policewoman," I said. "You will if she asks you to," Bea said. "For some reason I don't think you can hold a grudge even against your executioners, and I don't mean it as a compliment."

"You're right," I said that night while I wrote an apologetic letter to Nell. "It's one of my weaknesses."

During the evening we had a steady stream of curious visitors. Of the five-hundred-plus women in the building, the majority were in for streetwalking, drugs, or both, with the remaining few for petty and grand larceny and assault, and a tiny percentage on ten-day sentences for drunkenness, sleeping in the park, and so forth. There were no other call girls in the building and no one could remember there ever being any, so we were a great curiosity. Alice Joan, an unappetizing veteran streetwalker, brought her "girl friend," an equally grizzled specimen, in to look at us.

"I seen call girls come in on de 'tention flo'," she said wonderingly, "but dey gits out on bail an' de jedges doan give 'em no time." It was apparent they thought we had spit in the eye of the Vice Commissioner to get where we were. "Eben when I was workin' on de streets an' I was young an' had me a good pimp, dey didn't bother us none. Dey jest fills up dere quota wi' you when you ole an' doan have connections."

"What about Barbara?" Bea asked her. Barbara was obviously young and from what she said had been in jail some ten times. "Oh, *her*," Alice Joan said. "She doan have no pimp, honey. She got dat Cadillac fo' *herself,* an' she got a fur, *dis big,* but she doan want no pimp so's ebey once in a while she have to come to jail."

"How much you make a night?" the girl friend asked Bea. "On a *good* night, how much you make?" "I guess a couple of hundred dollars," Bea said. They laughed. "We makes more'n dat," Alice Joan said. "An' we doan eben git in de bed wit 'em. We gits dem up to de room an' when dey takes off dey close, we grabs dat wallet an' makes off." "You know how much Barbara makes a night, doin' dat?" the girl friend said. "Honey, dat girl gits de young ones wit *money*."

"Do all the streetwalkers steal?" Bea asked. "God yes," the girl friend said. "Men, dey picks you up on de streets, dey ain' gonna pay more'n two-three dollars. You *neber* make enough for yo' fix dat way." "We ain't bad," Alice Joan said. "You see dat woman dey call Mary-Helen 'round here, she an' dat bunch, dey gits dem men an' gives 'em de drops an' dat's de las' dey know."

A tremendous clanging started in the hot-water pipes and Alice Joan seized Bea's hairbrush from the table, pounded vigorously on the pipes and then stood on my bed and hollered "What you wan'?" down the ventilator. "Who dat?" a rather faint voice called. "It's *me*," Alice Joan yelled. "It's Alice Joan." "Well, go 'way from dat pipe," the voice came back, "I'm tryin' to call Bette." Alice Joan covered the vent with her hands and whispered, "Git ober here an' listen, it's dat Stud-Man Lillian callin' her woman."

Bea's face turned purple from suppressed laughter and she turned her head so I couldn't catch her eye. There was more banging on the pipe and a different voice, this time from above us, came through the vent and said, "If dat's you, Lillian, you kin jest stop because I'm still mad an' I ain't talkin' to you none good-by." The downstairs voice yelled, "You better talk to me 'cause I ain't jazzin' wit' you no mo'; iffen you wants ter break off wit' me you kin say so but I ain't takin' no jazz from you." There was a brief pause and a more humble voice from downstairs said, "Bette, are you listenin' to me?" After another silence the voice, almost pleading now, said, "Honey, are you listenin'?"

There was a long silence and a sobbing voice said, "I didn' mean ter call you no bitch." "You sorry?" the voice from upstairs said promptly. "I'm sorry," a little voice from downstairs said.

"Awright," the triumphant Bette said. "I ain' mad no

more, but I gotta go fix Nancy's hair so good-by." "Good-by, honey," the subdued Stud-Man Lillian said.

"Dey fights *all* de time," Alice Joan said, leaving the vent and sitting down. "You two better get you some good stud-men so's you have somebody ter fight wit'."

After the lights were out that night Bea said, "Do you suppose we're the only call girls in here because we're old and broken-down and don't have any connections?" "I think possibly connections have something to do with it," I said, "and when I get out I'm going to find out what happened." "Meanwhile you'd better git you a good stud-man to take your mind off things," Bea giggled.

There was a shower room in each corridor and they were easily the most uncomfortable spots in the building. Since the showers were always broken and dripping, the little cold, concrete shower rooms were overrun with fat black water bugs and filmy little silverfish with their many creepy legs which floated in the cracked floors and ran around the walls and dropped on you from the showerhead while you were bathing. After standing there through one lukewarm shower, flicking off bugs and shuddering at standing on a broken floor that held grooves of mud, I would in all likelihood have waited for my release to wash again had it not been for the social snobbery.

The gossips in each corridor managed to have cells near or preferably across from the shower room, and they kept an accurate account of who took a shower daily, and who showered three times a day, and who never bathed at all. Those who tried for the highest social standings made at least three trips a day down the hall with their soap, towel, washcloth and shower cap prominently displayed, and made very certain that they were seen going in, scrubbing and coming out. There was also much talk of "who kept a clean house" and who did not. Those who were vying for social position would make a major production of Saturday cleaning, and before eight o'clock I would awaken to sounds of heavy steel cots being dragged with a scraping and screaming of metal against concrete and slammed down in the corridor. Next, the various boxes and cartons that served as drawers were hauled out and piled on the cots and the cleaning would begin.

Granny lived diagonally across the hall from us and she had built a reputation for "having a clean house." After she removed her furniture she would carry a pail of boiling water, reeking of disinfectant, and go down on her hands and knees with a brush and scrub every inch of the floor, a process similar to scrubbing the sidewalk. Next she would take a new pail of water and the odiferous antiseptic and sterilize her walls, plunge both hands and a big rag in the toilet bowl and scour that, and finally open the corridor windows and vigorously shake the little ragged scraps of carpeting that served to cover a few inches of her floor. Every couple of weeks all her flopping shower curtains would be hauled down and others, stiffly starched, would take their place. This type of cleaning gave her a community reputation equivalent to that of a middle-class suburban matron who is active in church groups, entertains well and is famous for her apple pies.

Not only did Bea neglect to decorate our little home away from home, she also refused to clean it. "A jail cell is a jail cell," she would say, ignoring the horrified looks when she ground out a cigarette on our floor. Sitting on her bed she would prop her feet, not removing the heavy oxfords, on my bed and leave smears of mud on the already-filthy spread. Ignoring the possibilities of taking tiny scraps of material and fashioning a laundry bag, as some industrious souls spent their evenings doing, Bea simply threw dirty clothes in the corner, where they grew to a sizable pile. Instead of covering the little rusted metal table with a doily cut from the all-purpose shower curtains and trimmed with bright pink crochet, and then arranging the dime-store toilet articles from the commissary in a design, she just threw combs and brushes and piles of bobby pins and sometimes used Kleenexes in a heap. The gossips were utterly delighted; they had assumed that hundred-dollar-a-night call girls would go to great lengths to make their cell a palace of satin and lace. Their delight knew no bounds when the archfiend who lived across from the shower room reported that Bea never took a shower.

The answer to this was simple. Bea had taken a shower; in fact, she had taken one the first day, and had vowed then and there never to go back in the bug-infested little stall. Instead she would fill the sink with water and take a standing bath, which was considerably more trouble. Unfortunately, she took her bath in the morning before the gossips were abroad, and no one knew just how, and how often, she bathed.

Granny was the one elected to do something about the situation, and, since I was known as a clean person because I was seen entering the showers daily, I was called aside by Granny. I explained how Bea bathed and why, and Granny said, "How can she git *clean*, in dat little bowl?" "I don't know," I said, "but she's afraid of bugs and that's the way she does it every morning." "I see," Granny said thoughtfully, but I could tell she didn't believe such a story.

The next morning when the lights went on, Bea got up, made our tea and then filled the basin for her bath, and quite suddenly the hall was filled with curious faces. "What's the matter?" Bea said rather sleepily. "We jest want to see how you gonna git clean in dat little bowl," Granny said primly.

"I'm sorry I told them," I said later, after Bea had calmed down. "What could I have said?" "You could have told them to go drop dead," Bea said, "that's what you could have told them."

"Oh, to hell with what they think," I said. "Don't let it upset you." "It isn't that," she said, "it's just the whole *situation*."

That night, after we had got up for the sixth time to bang newspapers and chase mice off our beds, Bea said, "I don't think I'll live to get out of here." "You sound almost serious," I said. "Well, I don't mean I'm going to jump out the window," Bea said, "but I've never been so unhappy or depressed or hopeless in my life. Aren't you miserable?" I thought it over and replied, "No more than I have been."

Bea was horrified. "Oh, Ginny," she said, "that's insane. We had a beautiful apartment and we certainly didn't have to work much, and we could have almost anything we wanted; how can you say you're just as happy in a rat-infested cell and scrubbing floors?" "I didn't say I was as *happy*," I said, "I just said I was just as miserable. To me that apartment we lived in wasn't beautiful, it was cold-looking, and life here isn't any more purposeless than what I've been doing for the last six months."

"If I were out of here now," Bea said, "do you know what I'd be doing? I'd be taking a trip home to Colorado. I planned to take the children to see their grandmother, and I'd be up in the mountains." "If you were out of here now you'd be washing glasses for a bunch of drunks and passing out towels," I said. "You'd no more be in Colorado than I'd be in the cottage, looking at the lake. We both know what we want but we're in a rut."

"Well," Bea said, "when I get out I'm going to Colorado. I'm young and I'm going to make a list of the things I want to read and see and do in life and I'm going to follow it."

The next morning after Irma scrubbed my corridor for me I went to Mrs. Archibald, who was in charge of the second floor, and said I'd like to go into the library. "You are only supposed to go once a week," she said. "They call each floor once a week and you go into the library for a half hour." I went down to Captain White and she said, "I'll give you a note and you can use the library all you want, just don't mention it to anyone."

I found the library well stocked with books that were all clearly marked *Discard from Public Library*. The room was deserted except for members of the Friendly Visitors, a helping-hand group of volunteers who offered their services to the prison. Since the Friendly Visitors were considered unspeakable pests, they were shuffled off to the most isolated outposts—thus the library, where they arranged and rearranged books. In two and a half months I saw a handful of inmates and a surprising number of Friendly Visitors in the library, and everybody, including the volunteer women who were a bit skittish about close contact with prisoners, seemed happy with the arrangement.

While I was pulling books from the shelves, a Friendly Visitor approached me with appropriate caution and, standing at a distance designed to give her a head start in an emergency, said, "I've got some easy books with big print in the other room." I thanked her and went on pulling books and she said, "I've got magazines in the closet," and took me to a walk-in closet completely filled with back issues, some dating to the 1920's, of *The New Yorker*, the *Ladies' Home Journal*, and so forth. I carried a stack of them and a pile of books up to the cell, plumped up my straw mattress and pillow by banging them on the floor and settled down to read.

"This is absolute bliss," I remarked to Bea. "Maybe they'll let you stay here permanently," Bea said disgustedly. I got up and made tea with the boiling tap water and crawled back into bed. "I just might stay here," I said. " 'Stone walls do not a prison make, nor iron bars a cage, Souls innocent and quiet take . . .' "

"I wish I were in jail with Marcia," Bea said, walking out. "I'll bet she'd pace the floor with me."

The bliss was short-lived. For the first two days we had a steady stream of the curious walking back and forth past our cell and peeking in, which evidently did not satisfy them, for they devised a better way: They brought blankets, laid them in the corridor outside our cell and played poker, keeping an eye on us constantly. The din from five and six poker games running simultaneously, with interspersed fist fights, singing, arguments and shouting through the vents and to people in other corridors, was deafening.

"What you readin' in there?" someone would call in to me. "Why doan you stop readin' dat book an' play us some poker?"

At dinnertime they left briefly and returned with their tin trays, sat down on the blankets and picnicked. To attract our attention they slurped and slopped, banged their silver against the trays and dropped things with resounding bangs, always watching us from the corners of their eyes.

After dinner they announced they were going to play Truth or Consequences, or rather their own version of the game. It was simple in structure and transparent in purpose. One of them was appointed leader, and that person went around the group asking each member a personal question, such as "Who would you like to lay up with tonight?" or "Who was dat girl you was layin' up with on de fourth floor?" If the person refused to answer or told an obvious lie, the "consequence" was simply another, more personal question and the person was bound to answer. It was accompanied with great whoops of laughter and screams from the person who was being interrogated. After what they apparently considered a subtle length of time Bea and I were invited to play. I said I'd play some other time since I was writing a letter to my mother. Bea just said No.

After at least another hour, they decided to change the game to one called Group Therapy, the theme of the therapeutic discussion being Sex. The name was different but the game and its purpose remained the same. "Where do you suppose they learned the term 'Group Therapy'?" I asked Bea. "Oh," she said, "they have a psychology department here and Captain White told me something about a group-therapy project that meets twice a week." It was the first purposeful thing I'd heard of in the institution. From all I'd seen, the inmates spent their time, in some cases three years, playing poker, behind-the-outhouse games such as Truth or Consequences, knitting and engaging in bed activities to give grist to the mill for their question games. Their work consisted chiefly of sweeping and scrubbing the institution, ironing officers' uniforms, or learning to sew crooked seams on ancient sewing machines and turning out huge, unwearable bras.

The game changed again, this time to Yes, No, or Between the Sheets, the idea being to ask questions such as "Where was you and Mary las' night" that could not possibly be answered with anything but "Between the sheets." At eight thirty a good-natured little colored guard came and pulled the blanket from under them and chased them into their cells and threw the master switch. As soon as the lights went out the singing would start, each corridor having several performers who would sing requests. In our corridor we had an imitator of Sarah Vaughn who was excellent, a girl who did perfectly beautiful Dinah Washington selections and a large-breasted colored girl who did terrible renditions of "Over the Rainbow" and "You'll Never Walk Alone," with trills and much vibrato. I found that if I concentrated on the singing and ignored the patter of the mice I could fall asleep before the imitation of Sarah Vaughn's "Deep Purple" was finished.

The prison community, we had discovered, could almost have been divided into halves—Negro and Spanish—and the tiny white minority went along, for social purposes, with the colored since the Spanish were usually quite clannish and spoke their own language in their little cliques. Upstairs they took over one of the recreation rooms and danced and chattered to themselves. When Ethel Bettis' cellmate was released, one of the older Spanish women, committed on Welfare fraud for some confusion in her number of dependents, was put in with Ethel and for the first week slipped in and out of the cell as noiselessly as a ghost, getting up at six, scrubbing herself, kneeling and saying a brief rosary and going over to her Spanish friends. At night she would kneel on her bed and go over her beads in silence for over an hour, say good night very politely to Ethel and go to sleep.

One night she stopped at the end of a rosary service and said, "Ethel, why you do not sleep in a nightgown?" Ethel slept, like the rest of us, nude, because of the tremendous size of the cotton gowns and the fantastic amount of cheap starch that made them as crackly as a newspaper. "The gowns are uncomfortable," Ethel explained. "It's such a shame," the woman said sadly, "your Guardian Angel, he would like to sleep with you, but if you have on no clothes he would be ashame."

"I'm not going to sleep in one of those tents if I turn that angel against women altogether," Ethel said to me later, "but I'm sorry to insult that poor woman." "I'm surprised she cares about you *or* your angel," Bea said. The Spanish girls were usually quite hostile to the English-speaking; they had had some classic misunderstandings with the social workers and probation officers and often took it out on us.

One day I had tried to talk to a little Puerto Rican girl who was sitting in the corner of the ninth-floor recreation room crying, and she had simply turned her head away.

"She don't speak English good enough to talk to you," another girl had said. "What's the trouble?" I asked. "They just give her three months for streetwalkin'," she explained. "That damn probation officer's the one who did it—she tells the judge Maria's a bad girl. You see, when the probation officer talks to Maria, she asks her what she uster do in Puerto Rico, an' Maria says she steals. The officer gets mad an' says she's got to have respect an' not talk to her like that. Maria don't speak so good so she tells the woman she don't mean real stealing like from a store, she means steal from men, when they've got their pants off. The officer told her she was.

gonna tell the judge how bad she is and see she gets three months."

She looked over at the girl and added, "Anyway, it's better'n what coulda happened. Maria's only seventeen an' if they knew *that* she'd get four years in Westfield, but she tole 'em she was twenty-two an' they believe it 'cause she's got three kids."

Since most of the guards, social workers, probation officers and so forth were colored, the colored inmates had no problem in that direction. Among themselves they had several "family groups" in which there would be a grandmother and grandfather (usually a couple who had gone together for some time), a father and mother (again, a couple of long standing), many, many children and grandchildren and aunts and uncles. These cliques went into involved cousin and niece and nephew relationships with much incest and intrigue and shifting around of family positions in cases where grandfather and one of the granddaughters suddenly became involved and thus there was a shift in titles and the former grandmother might become an aunt.

On our floor a girl named Clara was Granny but Grandpa had been released just before we came and everyone was trying to help Clara find a replacement. Also there were many more "males" than "females" which meant almost everyone on the floor was called grandson, and in this particular family group, a "female" could only be admitted through marriage and so there were a few single colored girls who were yet to join the family. Shortly after we moved in we were invited to watch Granny perform a marriage between one of the grandsons, who already had several wives, and a very young and rather innocent girl who had been on the detention floor with us. After the ceremony, which consisted chiefly of "Do you take dis girl" and "Do you take dis man" and a final peremptory "Now kiss!", the new wife was given full family status and the first helping lesson was How to Boost.

This girl had never been to jail or, for that matter, any other institution, which made her almost as much a novelty as Bea and I. Not only had almost everyone been in jail be-tween five and fifty times, but it was usual to have started out in an orphanage or at least been committed to a Wayward or Incorrigible school before puberty. It was a rare person who hadn't spent most of her teens in Westfield, the New York State reformatory, or one of the Southern reform schools. With these backgrounds they were expertly smooth at steal-ing, which they called "boosting"; at hiding and smuggling objects and notes; at creating intoxicating messes from per-fume, bread, fruit, or for that matter anything but air; and at making institutional life existable, if not livable. The new wife had never stolen anything in her life, being from a middle-class background, and she was in jail only because the man she was dating had been stopped with marijuana which he promptly put in her pocket.

Now that she was in the family, Granny and Mary-Helen, who were both past masters at boosting, demonstrated to her how it was done. "Now, look at me," Mary-Helen said, com-ing down the corridor. "Am I walkin' like I always does?" "Yes," the girl answered. "Now I wan' you to look." Mary-Helen reached up under her skirt and pulled out a foot-high can of orange juice from the kitchen. "Now look again," she instructed. She reached up and replaced the can and then lifted her skirts to show it held firmly above her knees. "Now watch." She walked away down the corridor, turned and came back, without any indication that she held anything with her legs. "De elevator op'rator stop 'bove de flo'," Granny laughed, "an' she jest step up like nothin' wrong."

The girl was properly impressed and so was I. "You kin tote anything dat way," Mary-Helen said. "When I was firs' coming to jail, 'bout fifteen years ago, I took me a whole ham right outa de oben, an' I cart it dat way down de elevator.

'Most burn myself ter death too—I was jest hoppin' up an' down fo' I drops dat ham."

"Now," Granny said to the girl, "get goin' to de sewin' room an' I gonna show you how ter take you a wad a dresses an' come back wit' 'em."

The next day, Friday, my little corridor was scheduled for its weekly waxing and buffing, which involved using an ancient electric buffing machine that did nothing for the floor but was highly prized as a game device—one would steer the object and another would "ride" on it, planting one foot on each side and balancing with a great waving of arms and shouting and unnecessary falling off. Irma applied the wax and when I took the buffer from the broom closet I found I had a little line waiting to play. Bea had the same experience on the first floor and neither of us got through until after ten thirty.

After lunch Bea had little notes from her children thanking her for the letters telling all about Mexico, a letter from her grandmother in Colorado. I had a long letter from Nell.

There is no reason for you to become stagnant, Nell wrote. *You can get up each morning early and spend the day improving yourself. You can increase your spelling ability and your vocabulary. It is not necessary to simply sleep and read trash. You can* . . . From the illegibility of her penmanship I could tell the letter had been written while lying in bed. While I was still fired up with indignation I answered her letter.

I intend to spend the next three months, I wrote, *sleeping and reading back issues of the* Ladies' Home Journal. *I have spent twenty-five years improving each shining hour and this is where it's gotten me; I intend to enjoy the fruits of my labor. You spell like an illiterate and your letters are boring. Wish you were here.*

"Now that's a childish letter if I ever read one," Bea said. "You should be ashamed, being so vindictive." "That's right," I said happily and added a postscript, *This place is*

*full of conditions that should be changed and people who
need help. My abilities as a psychologist and teacher would
be indeed helpful. I am going to read every issue of* Ladies'
Home Journal *from 1921 on—if you save the world, write and
let me know how you did it.*

I dropped the letter in the chute and climbed into bed
with an illustrated Osa and Martin Johnson book and a cup
of tea. "Are you going to the dance tonight?" Bea asked me
much later. "I don't think so," I said, "I'm rather involved
in Africa and a small tribe of headhunters that hang alarm
clocks in their noses." "Oh, come on," Bea said. "If it's awful
you can come back down."

At six thirty the preparations for the dance began and
there was a great deal of running back and forth to borrow
socks and sweaters from people in other corridors and the
pipes banged constantly with girls calling those on other
floors to arrange dates. "Just like prom night in college," Bea
said, watching the crowd in the shower across the hall.

At seven thirty we went upstairs and found that we were
the only ones who had not dressed for the occasion. In addition to the starched dresses they had decorated themselves
as they did their cells—with everything handy. Those who
worked in the kitchen wore the white chefs' caps and aprons
over their dresses. Despite the heat in the dance room they
all wore sweaters and despite the time of year and the near
dark of the room almost everyone wore sunglasses with wildly
decorated frames. The "feminine" counterparts wore artificial flowers, ribbons and bows and the "males" wore their
hair slicked back, their dresses too stiff to allow sitting down,
and heavy black knee socks and V-necked sweaters their girl
friends had made for them. Bea wore her size-22 dress and I
wore a sadly limp sweetheart-necked dress with a busy pattern
of tiny green flowers and much green bias tape. "The way
we're dressed," Bea said, "it's hard to tell if we're 'men' or

'women.' " "As ugly as we look," I said, "who the hell would care?"

Apparently we didn't look too ugly to appeal to some, and we danced with quite a variety of women and received some further proposals.

"Do you know what they were doing outside?" Bea asked me later, "outside" referring to the roof adjoining the dance room. "I can guess from some of the invitations I got to go out there," I said.

I went to a dance tonight on a lovely roof terrace, Bea wrote to her children before bed.

On Saturday I stayed in bed until eleven, took a shower, made tea and resumed my cannibal story. At three Bea ran in with the newspapers and said, "It seems we're going to have company—look at this," and showed me a second-page story about a raid on a call flat in the East Seventies. There was a picture of two mink-coated women covering their faces with their coattails and a story about their arrest, nude, with two Johns. An opposite column gave the wire-tap evidence and below it was a story quoting Kennedy as saying there would be a city-wide cleanup following the Murrow broadcasts.

"Do you suppose the city will be hot now?" I asked Bea. "Oh, *hell*," she said, "do you know how many call flats are operating?" "No," I said, "but I can guess." "There are twelve major madams," Bea said, "who use about twelve to fifteen girls each, and there are at least a thousand girls who operate in the fifty to a hundred dollar bracket from their apartments. Now they've arrested two and you ask if they're going to clean up the city."

Late in the afternoon we were told the two girls, Viola and Sally, were in the building waiting for bail and if we went up on the roof we could see them. "I've seen enough prostitutes," I said, but Bea wanted to talk to them.

Sally, a little dark-haired girl who had worked for Lou just before Bea was there, told us that Viola had been bailed out a couple of minutes before and that she was waiting for her bond to be "processed." "That bunch of lying bastards," she said when we showed her the paper. "That whole wire tap is a lie and the whole damn story is a lie." "What do you think will happen?" Bea asked. "Nothing," Sally said. "We've got a good lawyer—we talked to him after the hearing this morning and he guaranteed to get us off for five hundred each." "That's not bad," Bea said. "We paid more than that and we're still sitting here."

"I can't understand that," Sally said. "We were over at Lou's the other night and everybody was talking about it. Were you kids paying off at all?" "No," Bea said. "Well," Sally said, "I didn't pay off for three years but just last year I made a deal for a hundred a month for Viola and me."

After Sally's bond came through, Bea and I walked out on the open roof, stood on a bench and looked out over the city. "If the mesh weren't here we'd have a good view," Bea said. It was very cold and there were a few snowflakes in the air and the lights were going on around the city. Far down below we saw a yellow Lincoln double-parked in front of the main entrance; in a few minutes Sally walked out and got in and they drove away. "What do you suppose will happen to them?" I asked Bea and she said, "Well, with the pay-off involved it should be interesting to see."

"New York is a beautiful city, isn't it?" Bea said. It was completely dark by then and we had buttoned the heavy sweaters and were still looking out through the wire. "When it's dark you don't notice the mesh," she said, "and you can see for miles."

Sarah, a very young, very masculine colored girl stopped in our cell before we went to bed and asked me if I intended to go to church the next morning. "No," I said. "Well," she said, "some of us are going to sing spirituals at the Salvation

Army meeting and I thought maybe you'd like to hear it." "I certainly would," I said.

"I can see you getting up at eight," Bea remarked when she left, "to listen to the Holy Rollers." "I'm not going to 'get religion,' " I said. "I love spirituals—I think it will be very stimulating." "They won't let you in with your hair that way," Bea said flatly. "People don't go to church without fixing their hair."

Before I went to bed, I got in the shower and washed my hair. "How are you going to set it?" Bea asked. "Don't be skeptical," I said. "I'm going to make Kleenex things and roll my hair on them and tie knots." "That's inventive," Bea said. "I'll let you do my hair, too."

When the lights went out, I was still doing Bea's hair and I finished it in the dark. Some time during the night I awoke to a violent banging and found Bea sitting up in bed, pounding on the wall with a rolled-up newspaper. Mice were running in frantic circles around the room; there were several on top of my blankets and a couple scrambling down from Bea's bed. All around the pillows and on the floor were little chewed-up bits of Kleenex from where the rodents had been eating our makeshift curlers. "Take the damn paper out of your hair," Bea said, yanking her curls down, "or they'll probably eat your hair too." I pulled what was left of my curlers off and we gathered up all the little pieces and threw them out the window. "That was a stupid idea," Bea said as we went back to sleep.

In the morning my hair was curled on one side and straight on the other and I went to church anyway. "Sure you don't want to go?" I asked Bea while I got dressed. "You don't know just *how* sure," Bea said.

The auditorium was large and the Salvation Army session must have been unpopular as there were just a handful of inmates scattered around in the damp, chilly room. After a considerable wait, two old ladies in Salvation Army uniforms came in with three very small Puerto Rican children. The women fussed around with the speaking stand, lights and piano for a while and then one set up the microphone and said her name was Colonel Gotz and her very *good* friend, and companion for *many* years, Colonel Hamm, was going to tell everybody how she came to join the Salvation Army.

Colonel Hamm thanked her and said that she was happy to be there and she wanted to tell about how she came to join the Salvation Army. It was a long story, ranging from the time she and her sister had seen the Salvation Army on the street and later that night she had gone back to hear more, through her joining and her many happy years full of blessings she had had in the Salvation Army. One of the typical miracles of her life was receiving five dollars from her mother just when she had been walking around with a hole in her shoe for three months, and she knew God prompted her mother to send the five dollars, with which she bought new shoes Praise Be to the Lord. "The Lord will always give you bread," she said. "Sometimes there might even be a little jam on the bread and sometimes not, but the Lord will always give you bread." Indicating her arm, which was in a sling, she announced that through the mercies of the Lord, in her recent fall she had broken not two arms but only one, Praise Be to the Lord, and therefore could still play the piano, and she climbed painfully from the piano, lifted the lid, and after her friend lined the little Puerto Ricans up, proceeded to play with her good hand while they sang a hymn in Spanish.

"Praise Be to the Lord, Praise Be to the Lord," she murmured afterward, clambering up the stairs to the speakers' stand.

The meeting was long and dragged through unintelligible prayers and Spanish hymns and much complimentary chit-chat between the little old women. At the end of the program Sarah and four other colored girls appeared and sang three spirituals with a jazz beat and it was indeed worth hearing but I was so exhausted and chilled that I hardly heard them.

Bea was still in bed when I got back to the cell and she looked up and said, "Was it worth it?" "It was *not*," I said, "and it was a disgrace. There's no reason to let every damn bunch of do-gooders come into a prison; if they can't provide something worth while, groups like that shouldn't make an open house." "You *are* wound up," Bea said, pulling the covers over her head. "Go back to sleep." "I will not," I said. "I'm going to write to Commissioner Kross and tell her what I think of giving prisoners nothing to do but scrub floors and listen to any unintelligent, fundamentalist garbage that . . ." "I thought you wanted a vacation," Bea said. "Read your magazines."

I got out my stationery from the commissary—conveniently lined foolscap—and wrote a letter to Commissioner Kross. *I do not feel that if the penal system cannot provide suitable facilities they should allow unsupervised, volunteer groups to give the inmates a more discouraging program than they already have,* I wrote, and the letter continued on and on. When I got through I read it to Bea and she said, "That's nice but I thought you didn't care. Anyway," she said, "do you know what she'll do with that letter?"

All day Sunday I wrote bitter letters to the editors of the New York papers. "By the way," Bea said mildly as I was sealing envelopes, "you don't really think the censors will let those out of here, do you?"

It honestly hadn't occurred to me that the censoring board would stop the letters as surely as they had blocked out the entire section of a letter to Nell where I told about having pig tails and beans for dinner. "By God, I'll get them out of here some way," I said. "You could send them out the way Pat sends hers," Bea suggested.

Pat Murphy was a brawny Irish girl who was in for pushing drugs; every day the little blond streetwalker she lived with in the "streets" would drive up in her convertible, pause across the street on the Sixth Avenue side, and Pat, standing on the tenth floor, would sail a letter secured to a bar of soap into the open car. "You'll kill someone," I had said the first time I saw her winding up for the pitch. "Who the hell cares?" she said, firing away with astounding aim that plopped it right into the back seat.

"I'll find a better way than that," I said. "I'll find a way to get these letters out of here and I'll write about every skeleton in every closet in this building and I'll get that out, too." It infuriated me to suddenly realize that I was, for all good purposes, incommunicado.

"I wish I could think of some way to help you," a girl who was a Vassar graduate said when I told her about the letters, "but it's difficult. There are several guards who mail letters but someone on the outside would have to meet them and arrange to pay for it." "I think I'll just wait till I'm out of here," I said, "and write a book."

The news traveled with the rapidity common to all institutions and the next day Captain White said rather sadly, "I hear you are going to write a book about us." "I am," I said, "I certainly am." "I hope you'll include some of the nice things," she said, "such as the beauty parlor and . . ." She hesitated perceptibly and added, "There are many things we are trying to do." Before I left her office, she said, "We have a psychology department here." "You certainly don't advertise where it's located," I said and was informed that it was around the corner from the library and I was welcome to go see it.

It was as empty as the library and in three little offices sat three psychologists.

A short man with horn-rimmed glasses who sat in the office nearest the door looked up and said, "Hi, I'm Mr. Donnell and you must be Virginia McManus." I must have looked surprised for he added, "News travels fast around here—I know all about you." "I know all about you too," I said, and told him about the Group Therapy game. He roared and said "I hope we do a little better than that in the sessions down here. What can I do for you?" "Well," I said, "I'm just making a general tour of the building." "Fine," he said, "come down here any time. You can talk or get your head shrunk or just gather material for your book."

"News *does* travel fast," Bea remarked when I told her about it. "Incidentally, Harly will be here at four." "I won't see him," I said automatically. "It was all right when we were in our own clothes but I'll be damned if I'm going to let Harly see me in this getup and with my hair like this." "Go to the beauty parlor," Bea said. "Tell them your attorney's coming and see if they'll do something with your hair."

At three thirty, when I came down from the beauty parlor, Bea took one horrified look at me and said, "You look exactly like Vi." My hair was arranged in a series of crimped, narrow waves after the old marcel fashion and my head appeared as smooth and oval as an egg. "Why in the *world* did you have them do that?" "I didn't have them do that, that's all they know how to do," I said. "It's supposed to be a training school for beauty operators and the instructor is the one who did this as a demonstration." "Well, brush it out quick," Bea said.

At four o'clock, I was still brushing and the waves were as tight, stiff and resistant as ever. "I think the woman has discovered the only *permanent* wave," Bea said. "You'll have to wet it."

I dampened my hair and brushed and when I stopped each wave slithered back into position. When the guard announced that Harly was downstairs, Bea was pouring cupfuls of water over my head while I leaned over the basin.

"Jesus Christ," Harly said, looking at my dripping hair and my catalogue dress. "Have they been working you over with the hose?" "No," I said, "but when I get out of here I'm going to see why they're using state funds to hire an incompetent instructor and . . ." "Relax," Harly said, "I've got lots of news. For one thing Judge Wahl awarded you fifteen hundred dollars on the Kouberoff suit." "How *wonderful*," Bea said. "And," Harly continued, "when Judge Wahl read about your arrest he said that you were a tarnished jewel and took the award back." "See what I told you?" I said to Bea.

Harly had lots of other news. He said that Sally and Viola had been released that morning for lack of evidence; that we had been evicted from the building on "moral" grounds and God knows where the clothes and furniture would go; that the FBI wanted to question us because one of the men in our apartment had been involved in a stock swindle; that the Attorney General's office wanted to see us about the same matter; that the Treasury Department would be over to talk to us about taxes.

"Why did they release Sally and Viola?" I said. "They had enough wire-tap evidence to hang them." "They don't convict call girls in this city," Harly said. "And just what the hell are we?" I asked. "I don't know," Bea said, "but I think the word is 'patsy.' Once in a while somebody has to go—remember the political rhyme: 'What a nice man is Willy Bly. He took the rap for you and I.' "

Back in the cell, Bea had a letter from her grandmother and I had one from Nell with a typed note from Nonnie included. *Heard from your cousin Ginger, today,* Nonnie wrote. *She has such a satisfying life—to you I suppose it would seem dull. She is just a wife and mother, but some people can find complete happiness in just leading a decent, useful life, contributing to society.* . . . "Goddamn her," I said, tearing up the letter. "Goddamn her to hell and I mean it." "Calm down," Bea said, "and I'll read my grandmother's letter to you."

" 'Your brother and his wife came to see me for my birthday,' " she read. " 'They own their own home now and have two fine children. *They may not be rich but they are lead-*

ing good lives. They came for a week and they went on to Florida; they don't have much but they *save and are thrifty,* and *she sews clothes for her and the children* and shops savingly and is such a good woman and they *drove me to church* and *gave me ten dollars for the plate. . . .'* Had enough?" Bea asked. "Quite enough," I said. "But did your grandmother spend fifteen years telling you how undesirable marriage was? Did she tell you how vile and corrupt men were? Did she detest your grandfather? I can accept almost anything but hypocrisy and that is the one unforgivable trait."

"Here's one more hypocrisy," I said later, reading the newspaper account of Sally's and Viola's acquittal. Next to their story was an article describing the special telephone line the police had set up to handle phone tips the public might care to make, informing on the whereabouts of call girls. "It might take the place of witch hunts," Bea said.

Chapter 15

We had now been in jail a month, and time hung heavily on our hands. "How can a person survive this for three years?" Bea asked on a dark, rainy afternoon as she paced back and forth in the little cell. At the end of the corridor, in what was euphemistically called the "recreation room," a group had been playing "Send My Bail to the Tiajuana Jail" over and over on the scratchy little phonograph; a few people were standing on the toilets in order to see out the windows and watch the construction across the street and many were asleep. A little group that had been playing poker in the corridor had given up and was gazing out the hall window at the downpour.

"Look at dat drunk man," one of them said. "Come outa dat bar and he about to fall over." "I wist it were me," someone said, sincerely, and the corridor went back to silence.

At the end of the hall, Irma, who was locked in as punishment for throwing hard-boiled eggs at someone in an attempt to break the "eye" they were putting on her, announced loudly, "I'm fixin' to sing." Irma had kept the entire floor awake the night before with her "protest singing" which ranged from some dirge about "Jesus Be My Help" to "When My Sugar Walks Down the Street." "You better not start that again," Marie hollered. "We hear nuff a yo craziness las' night." "Jesus he take care a me an' you kaint do me no harm," Irma shouted back and began to sing the religious dirge.

"Oh shut up your noise," a girl named Myrt called from her end of the corridor. Now that Irma was locked in there was much bravery in insulting her. The dirge went on.

"I sure wish I had me a fix," Myrt said sadly. "Me too," several echoed. "When I get in dem streets, I'm gonna git me a fix fore I ever speaks to my ol' man," Myrt said. "I'm gonna git me some coke and snuff it up my nose, and I'm gonna git some horse an' shoot it, an' den I'm gonna go git all the pork chops I kin eat." "God yes, baby," Mary-Helen said. "I doan git outer here ten minutes fore my man gits me a fix. I tells him, if I serves time fo' yo, least you can do is git me a fix when I'm cut loose." "Jo," Myrt yelled down the corridor, "you through wit dat book 'bout de pusher?" "Yeah," Jo yelled back, "you kin come an' git it."

"Wouldn't you suppose they'd want to read something else?" Bea whispered to me. Ignoring the library books completely, the girls passed around a handful of ragged, torn paper-back books about dope, rackets, prostitution, jails and so forth. Myrt had come in once and looked at the book I was reading and said, "What do yo' wanta read that stuff fo'? I got a book 'bout a call girl you can have." "This is a book about a call girl," I said. (It was *Cast the First Stone*) "Ain't it a library book?" Myrt said. "They've got books about prostitutes in the library," I said. "They've got books about gangsters, and almost everything." "Well," Myrt said, "I wouldn't know how to fine nothin' down there."

"It wouldn't hurt to show them how to use the library," I

had remarked once to Mr. Donnell, and he had said, "That's right, but who's going to show them?" "I would," I said, "but I'm hardly in a position to. They resent it enough that I'm an inmate and I *read* 'literary' books; I don't want to push the resentment any further." "I think you're right," he said. "If you were going to be here longer you could work around to all kinds of things—you could teach and so forth—but in a short time it would be impossible."

Just after we sat down to dinner Tuesday evening the sounds of a good-sized battle floated up from the sixth-floor dining room through our open windows. It started with a couple of sharp reports that must have been plates thrown against the wall, and almost at once there was a violent splintering of wood as chairs were slammed down on the tables. There were crashes as tables went over and broke more crockery and the sound of tin trays landing and an increasing din over shouted obscenities and vulgarities. Everybody in our dining room rushed to the windows and crowded to see the silverware flying from the sixth floor to the street and our dinner was completely forgotten in the excitement of a riot.

After about five minutes of pitched battle it was apparently over and dinner was eaten with much speculation about what had happened and why and much veiled hoping that there had been bloodshed. "I'd hate to be a guard on the sixth floor," Bea remarked to Barbara. "God yes," she said. "Those ditty-bops half-kill a guard if they get hold of one."

It was apparent that the ditty-bops, the sixteen-, seventeen- and eighteen-year-olds, were more dangerous in a group than singly, for, individually, they were a scrawny and pitiful-looking lot indeed. One, a butchy little girl of about seventeen, had stood next to me in the clinic line and said, "My name is Lee but they call me Diabolo. It means devil," she added, in case I wasn't impressed by the connotation. She and her girl friend, a simple-looking fat child with curly hair, had been "kicked out" of Westfield as incorrigibles and had to serve their time in the House of Detention. "We did awful things up there," the girl friend, Sara, giggled. "There was one guard we didn't like and one night when she was in charge we all started singing 'A Hundred Bottles of Beer on the Wall' and we sang it right down to 'No Bottles of Beer on the Wall.' She couldn't make us stop, and when she called the other guard we all yelled." "Yeh," Diabolo said, "and we used to take kids' shoes and hide them all over and once we tied knots in some kids' underwear and wet it, and you shoulda seen 'em trying to get them knots out."

"My God," I said to Bea, "that's just summer-camp stuff. Since when is that incorrigible?" "Well," Bea said, "when they get here and don't have anything to do they think of more advanced things."

Stories drifted upstairs to the effect that the ditty-bops were protesting having to go to bed at eight fifteen, even on Saturday night. It had been a sore point for quite a while, and since the days were longer, and we were in bed before it was completely dark, there was usually an hour of noise from the sixth that kept the whole building awake. One night they had lighted pillowcases and sailed them from windows, causing a near panic on Sixth Avenue and making me vow never to walk under jailhouse windows, if and when I were ever in the free world again.

"You know," Barbara said after dinner, "my grandmother used to say, 'The devil finds work for idle hands,' and I never knew just what she meant until I saw those ditty-bops." "What do they do all day?" Bea asked her, and Barbara said, "They do just what we do, they sit around and play poker and Truth or Consequences. It's not so bad for us because we're grown people and we know when we get out we've got stuff to do, but those kids don't have anything."

Later that evening the conversation in the hall droned on; they were playing the familiar game of "What I'm going to do when I get out." It never varied—they were going to get a fix, a hamburger, a trick to pay for another fix, and another hamburger. "God," one said, "fore they gits me back here agin I'm gonna snuff up all de cocaine in New York." "Me too," said Matilda. "I'm gonna git me a trick an' take ev'ry penny that bastard's got an' buy up all de cocaine my pusher's got."

Matilda was a middle-aged white woman but she spoke with a Negro accent; she came to jail six and seven times a year, spending only a few days in the streets in between. This had gone on for years and Matilda had become stir crazy; she'd developed a strong colored accent, talked about nothing but drugs although she was never "out" long enough to have a habit. She spent hours pulling at the bars on her cell door, causing the door to clank heavily, and shouting a steady jargon that consisted chiefly of "Jesus come to me . . . oh Lord . . . Jesus *come to me* . . . oh, these damn bastards . . . oh Lord oh Lord . . ." She had left two weeks after we came in and was picked up again and back in three days.

"Oh, I gotta stay out long enough to git me some cocaine *this* time," she said now. "Oh, *this time* I gotta stay out an' git me some cocaine." "Dey ain't gonna git me fo' a year," Myrt said. "Dis time I'm gonna stay in dem streets a year. I ain't gonna do nothin' but eat pork chops an' snuff dat cocaine an' . . ."

"I wish this were a radio program and I could turn it off," Bea said. We were trying to read in bed and the conversation was distracting. The sheets were damp, the rooms were damp to a point of beads of moisture forming on the walls, the bugs were running rampant since they had been flooded from their hiding places and a strong scent of mildew hung over the cell. "I'll make some tea," I said, tea and cigarettes being the only bright spots in our lives. "When I get out of here . . ." Bea began. "Get you some cocaine and snuff it up your nose," I suggested. "No," Bea said, "and I'm not dreaming of pork chops. When I get out of here I'm going to live.

This is like a living death and I'm going to travel and find a career and I'm going to *live* before I get to the old people's home and this is all I have left."

By late afternoon it was completely dark outside and the rain came down in great gushes and the damp and boredom seemed almost unbearable. We turned out our light, took aspirins and went to sleep. When I awoke sometime after midnight I had a terrific headache, my back was stiff and my throat was dry and I had trouble swallowing. I took more aspirins and Bea said, "I feel horrible, give some aspirins and some cold water to me." "Good Lord," I said, "you don't suppose we've caught something, do you?" "I wouldn't know," Bea said. "I feel as though I've got the flu."

Back in bed, I felt absolutely terrified. A few days before, Nell had written and said, *Please take care of yourself and try not to get sick. It has occurred to me that if you should become ill and die I would have to go through life explaining that my only daughter died in prison. I don't think I could bear the shame of it.* At the time I had been both amused and angry at her attitude, but now it occurred to me that I, too, would not like to have me die in prison—not because of public attitude but simply because I didn't want to die in the first place, and also I had been making plans for my future and it would seem ironic to die just when I was determined to make something of my life.

And I knew what sort of treatment you could expect in an emergency. Martha, a colored woman in her eighth month of pregnancy, had developed some sort of complication that the clinic upstairs refused to treat, and they wouldn't let her go to Bellevue. In desperation she had set her cell on fire, almost burning to death when the cell door stuck and she couldn't be released at once. The prison had to send her to Bellevue as a suicide attempt.

There were other ways devised to get to Bellevue. Since the prison was much more afraid of erratic behavior than germs, most of the women faked dangerous insanity when they were physically sick. Mary-Helen got to the hospital to have ingrown toenails treated by carrying a huge pail of garbage into her cell, dumping it all over the floor and playing in it. After several guards had tried to stop her, and were covered with a mixture of beans and coffee grains for their efforts, she was sent over to the Bellevue Psychiatric Ward, checked and found sane, given a minor toenail operation and some antibiotics. She returned in triumph.

I wondered just what type of insanity I could fake if I were really ill. I finally drifted off to sleep planning schizoid activities.

In the morning Bea and I awoke with deep, barking coughs; the rain continued, the bugs scampered in droves looking for dry spots, and we were sick. Bea stayed in bed and I went to the clinic. "Have you ever had female trouble?" the doctor asked me. "No," I said, "but I've got the flu now." "Well," she said, "I can give you sulfa if you want some, and when you are better I can examine you internally and perhaps you have some female trouble that is lowering your resistance."

I took the sulfa and went down to Mr. Donnell and said, "In case I get actually sick can you get me into Bellevue?" "What did the doctors in the clinic say?" "She said when I felt better she'd examine me internally." He laughed and said, "If you ever really got sick I would see that you were taken care of." I went back to bed, considerably relieved that I wouldn't disgrace my family by dying in chains.

That afternoon Johanna Martin and Mrs. Barrington, a very young call girl and her very old (seventyish) madam, were brought in and I talked to them while they were waiting to get out on bail. Mrs. Barrington was tiny and very frail and so nervous that she had forgotten her attorney's phone number and was making a great fuss trying to remember it. The girl stared out the window and Mrs. Barrington wept and dug in her cluttered handbag for the elusive number. "I am so sorry for you, my dear," she told me before she left. "So many of us are so sorry for you." "It really isn't that bad here," I said. The sulfa was causing a ringing and buzzing in my ears that was almost deafening and I was anxious to get back to bed. "Well," she said, "you are being quite brave about it but I've been in business thirty-five years and you are certainly being made an exception."

Since our arrest there had been twelve other call-girl apartments raided and all the girls had been either acquitted or given suspended sentences. "Do you think you'll do any time?" I asked her. "No," she said, "and I'll see that my girl doesn't either. I'm so sorry for her," she added. "She's a nice girl and they lied so about her."

I went back to bed and all evening I lay on the damp sheets and watched the bugs and listened to the rain and the high-pitched ringing from the sulfa. "I'm going wild with it," I told Bea. "It was against my better judgment to take the sulfa anyway; I don't think that woman knows what she is doing." It had been the same doctor who insisted Bea was pregnant two months before, and who told another woman, who was in for forgery and had never hustled, that she had better stop streetwalking before her "uterus fell out."

"What do you think can happen from an overdose of sulfa?" Bea said. "I don't know," I said, hearing my own voice as very faint and far away, "but I'm not taking any more to find out."

In the early evening Myrt came in to see how I was and invite me to a nutmeg party. "I'm better and what's a nutmeg party?" I asked, fascinated with the way my voice seemed to bounce, like a ventriloquist's.

"You just sniffs nutmeg," Myrt explained simply. "Miz Burt gits it fo' us." Miss Burt was the music teacher, a little twitching wreck of a woman who came in twice a week and led a choral group in "Softly, As in a Morning Sunrise," and she was considered crazy and few people went. She was fussy and nearsighted and reminded me of the Dean of Women in my undergraduate college who used to warn the girls never to wear red "because it makes men passionate" and "never wear patent-leather shoes because they're like a mirror and men can see under your skirt." Apparently she wasn't nearly as prudish as she looked if she supplied them, as Myrt said she did, with the forbidden nutmeg, or perhaps she was so innocent she didn't know its use.

From the room at the end of the corridor I could hear the hysterical shrieks that indicated nutmeg was being sniffed. "I think it would kill me," Bea said weakly. "I'm still buzzing from that damned sulfa." "I'll try it if you will," I said. "It won't hurt none," Myrt said.

At least fifteen women were crowded into the little cell; tears streaming down their faces, they sniffed the nutmeg from the back of their hands or drank it mixed with a little hot water from the tap. I tried drinking it and it was similar to drinking a thick mixture of rust and water and stuck in my already-sore throat.

Myrt giggled and said, "It taste nasty but it sho will make you high." Bea sniffed some and went into a violent fit of sneezing. "You doan sniff no coke, I kin see dat," Mary-Helen said.

"I'll never be an addict," Bea said, collapsing into her bed. "Neither will I," I said. I could feel particles sticking in my throat and it burned. "Why do you suppose they're doing that?" Bea asked, blowing her nose. "Nothing better to do," I said. It was true—to fight off the monotony they would try almost anything. Three times a day when clinic was called, almost everyone would line up and collect pills—aspirin, sleeping pills, cold tablets, pills for indigestion—and then hoard them until they had a couple of dozen to be taken at once.

"When I was a child," Bea said, "and we lived out in the

country, my cousin and I got so bored we used to hold our noses and spin around to get dizzy." "At least that isn't still your idea of a party," I said. "I used to swing up and down on the in-a-door bed but I can think of more important things to do." "Not in here," Bea said. "I wish we had a nice in-a-door to swing on."

The next morning my ears were still buzzing and ringing, my cough was deeper and more congested and I was light-headed with fever. I went up to the clinic for more aspirin and the nurse said, "I'll bet you've got flu. We've got two hundred cases so far."

As I walked through the corridors going back to bed I could hear violent coughing and sneezing from almost every cell. "Maybe we should take more sulfa," I suggested to Bea. "I'd rather die of pneumonia than sulfa poisoning," she said. "I don't trust anything but aspirin in here."

By late afternoon our fevers were high and I was lying in a limp heap when I got a letter from Nell saying:

We hope you will admit you've made a mess of your life. Please do not *let yourself go* even if you are in prison. *Brush your hair* and get plenty of rest. From your pictures you are gaining weight—do exercises twice a day, watch what you eat, and try to get your hips and waist slimmed down. When you get out you'll want to be ready to get to work *at once*. We want you to do something that we can *brag* about—we are so tired of having to lie about what you're doing and cover up and of never having anything good to tell. You'll have to accomplish a great deal to make up for this disgrace.

We want you to come home for a while where we can *help* you. At least we expect you to come home for a visit *at once* when you are released.

Enclosed was a letter from Nonnie that said:

We do not feel from the tone of your letters that you intend to change, and if you come home to see your mother I will simply take a trip until you've gone.

"You know," I said to Bea, "I feel like a worm with a robin on each end." "I feel," Bea said hoarsely, "like I'm dying."

I got up and dressed with very shaky hands and went down to Mr. Donnell's office. I handed him the letter and said, "It may just be that I'm sick and can't cope with normal situations but I think these letters are part of a psychological warfare plan to drive me crazy." He read them and said, "Why do you keep on reading their letters? You could just tear them up." "I used to do that," I said, "but it made me feel too guilty. After all, look at how much I've *done* to these people." "Nonsense," he said. "Look how much these people have done to you. Why don't you think about yourself and what you want and not think about other people for a while?" "I don't want to think about myself," I said. "It makes me ill." "Do you want to go home when you get out?" he asked. "My God no," I said. "I want to go away and begin my life over and I don't want advice on being rich and successful and making them happy. I just want to see if I can find a quiet beach and a little house and teach or write and have some peace." "Tell them so," he said. "Write and tell them you want to lead your own life and you don't give a damn about fashions and to worry about themselves."

While I was waiting for an elevator to go back upstairs some prisoners from Riker's Island came past carrying garbage. They were wearing the uniform of the men's prison—khaki pants and big, coarsely knit sweaters in a strange mustard brown and I thought, Ann would have loved that outfit. I remembered the fight she and Nell had when Nell criticized her sports clothes and I giggled to myself.

I don't want to come home until I've rebuilt my life, I wrote to Nell. *It will be difficult enough and this time I must do things my own way.* While I wrote I tried not to think of Nell's reaction when she read it. She may say I'm all she has, I thought, but she's got Nonnie and my father. I'm the one that is actually going to be alone. It just occurred to me that I was to be completely alone when I got out.

For almost a week I was too sick to really care where I was, and since almost everyone else was sick too, the institution was quiet and I slept and drank tea and took aspirins and slept. On the first of April I awoke with a wonderful surge of health and energy. "It looks like spring outside," I told Bea. "How do you feel?" "Much better," she said. "I feel wonderful," I said. "I'm going to get up and take a cold shower and *accomplish* things." "What the hell are you going to accomplish?" Bea asked with understandable skepticism.

I stood up on the toilet and opened our cell window as far as it would go and stood sniffing the spring air. "If I were home now," I said to Bea, "I'd go down to the cottage and take off the shutters and sweep and paint—I love to paint outdoors in the spring." "You are in jail," Bea said, "and there isn't a thing you can do." "I can plan," I said. "For once I can sit down and plan the rest of my life. I'm away from the people that bother me, I've got twenty-five days more of being fed and put to bed and relieved of responsibility and I can decide what I really want." "I know what I really want," Bea said, "and it begins with getting the hell out of here."

I dressed and went up on the roof and looked out over Greenwich Village. It was Saturday and the Village had come to life; the fruit stand across the street had bunches of flowers in pails and the artists had set up their canvases on Sixth Avenue and it looked like a very idealistic poster of the Left Bank in Paris. It was suddenly warm and sunny and the old gray tomcat from the seventh floor lay in perfect ecstasy and I was tempted to join him. Two girls from "seven" who had brought the cat up for his airing were sitting on a bench knitting and one of them said to the other, "How many mo' days you got?"

I was overwhelmed with a desire to get out. I had had enough of looking out through mesh and bars. I wanted to get in a car and drive away from this damp, dull world where I had been confined for almost two months and away from the poor, dull souls in it—I wanted to get out to the ocean and run down a beach and shake off the mildew of the entire experience. "I want to get out of here," I said to Bea, who was still in bed, when I went downstairs. "Well, I'll be damned," Bea said. "You can come up with some good ideas."

"I don't think I can sit here for another twenty-five days," I said to Mr. Donnell. "What are you going to do when you get out?" he asked. "I'm going to get on a plane," I replied, "and go to San Francisco and for one week I'm going to sit and look at the ocean. Then I'm going to find a house on a beach, as far away from people as I can get, send for my cat and my books, and write." "Do you really think you'll do it?" he asked. "I don't mean to act doubting, but do you think you'll go through with it?" "I think so," I said. "I doubt if I would have before, but now that I've hit rock bottom and have to move in some definite direction and haven't a tie in the world, I think I'll go through with it." We sat in silence for a moment and I added, "But I think I'll lose my mind waiting twenty-five days."

"You weren't having any more satisfaction in the twenty-five days *before* you came to jail than you're going to have in the next twenty-five, so you can stand it," he said. I knew what he meant—once when I had said I didn't think I could live through it he had told me about an experience the Christmas before when a rather beautiful colored girl had been weeping in his office. "I can't live through Christmas in jail," she had said. "I can't stand Christmas with bars and guards and locks." Mr. Donnell said that he was genuinely touched and he had said, "Where were you last Christmas?" She had replied through tears, "I was in a little hotel room on Forty-seventh Street—my pusher died in Bellevue from tetanus and I couldn't get a connection and so I had to kick the habit alone, and then by New Year's I had enough strength to eat a sandwich, and go out and turn a couple of tricks and I found a new pusher and got a fix and then everything was all right."

"You mean," Mr. Donnell said, "that you spent last Christmas alone in a flea-bag hotel room, without food, violently sick?" "Yes," she said. "Well," Mr. Donnell said, "this Christmas you're in excellent health, you're surrounded by friends, you've got a lover, you'll have a Christmas dinner and since your family knows where you are you'll get Christmas cards. You are better off than last year so enjoy yourself."

"I know that sickness and freedom can be better than health and bars," Mr. Donnell had said when he told me the story, "but still most of these people who count the days to get out are really less tense, better fed, and have more laughs here than when they're being chased and hunted in the streets."

"I know what you mean," I said to him, "and I've told you that jail isn't any more boring or aimless than what I was doing in that apartment with Bea Garfield, but now that I know I'll have something else I can hardly wait, I can barely sit here." "You'll live," Mr. Donnell said. "Plan what you're going to write about. By the way, just what *are* you going to write about?"

"I suppose I'll write about this, at first," I said. "I'm so disgusted with so much I've seen here I'll have to write it and get it out of my system. But there are many things I've half-planned to write and never had time to do anything about."

Chapter 16

OUR DISCHARGE DATE was April 22, and five others on our floor were scheduled to leave that morning. Every Thursday little yellow slips of paper were sent around to new inmates, telling them the total number of days they were to serve and the day on which they could leave, and there was a great rushing around to find others who were leaving on the same day. Carlotta, an unattractive, heavy girl in our corridor, decided that our mutual discharge date gave us some bond of kinship and two weeks before, she began daily trips to my cell to discuss "plans for leaving."

"What are you going to wear home?" she asked on her first visit. "Well," I said, "I have the suit I wore in downstairs, and I guess I'll wear that." That obviously didn't involve enough festivity to please her. "You get someone to bring you other clothes," she said. "My boy friend always brings me a different outfit." "All right," I said, merely to end the discussion since I still intended to wear the black suit. "We'll go out and have a drink," she said. "You and my boy friend Al and me. We'll go right out and have a beer."

"How do I get out of that?" I asked Bea. "If anything could take the thrill from my release it would be having a beer with Carlotta and her pimp at nine A.M."

"What do you want to do when you get out?" Bea said.

"*Leave*," I said. "I want to take a cab to the airport and go directly to the Coast and start from there."

"That would be fine," Bea said, "if you were an insect and could just flap your wings and go from place to place, but since you're human there's a little matter of getting our clothes from storage, and you have clothes at Kouberoff's, and getting money out of banks . . ."

"Oh, *shut up*," I said. "You're spoiling everything."

A week before the Great Day, Carlotta set her hair in seemingly thousands of tiny pin curls and said, "I'm going to leave it up until The Morning and wait till you see how curly it will be." "Does it take a week to curl it?" I said. "I just can't wait to start getting ready," she said. "This makes the time seem closer." "I guess tomorrow she'll take her pre-release bath," Bea said. "It still seems a long time to me." "A week isn't long," I said, "and I'm beginning to get excited about it."

The Friday before our discharge we were so jumpy we went to the movie, something we usually scorned since the choice of films was poor and the equipment broke down as many as fifteen times during one showing, making it necessary to turn on all the lights, and then the film would start at the wrong place. It was a cowboy picture with much emphasis on good men and bad men and the audience necked away in the dark room and completely ignored the screen until a very innocuous love scene between a gingham-dressed woman and the hero came on and then the light hand-holding was greeted with wild catcalls and shouted suggestions. When the plot returned to the pursuit of the outlaw everyone went back to necking.

Bea and I squirmed and wriggled in our hard chairs, both with boredom caused by the film and nervousness and impatience caused by counting days. We left before it was over and went back to our cell.

"I wish I had a Scotch and water," Bea said passionately. "I want champagne," I said, "and a steak. I don't care if it is morning when I get out." We stood on the toilet and looked out the window at the Friday-night crowd on Sixth Avenue. "Does it seem *possible*," Bea said, "that in four days we'll be out? Does it seem possible we'll walk down that street and be absolutely free, and we can go any place we want and drink?" I was suddenly overwhelmed with the joy of getting out. "It's like being reborn," I said, and Bea agreed.

The next three nights I had difficulty sleeping. I would awake over and over during the night and think about the wonders of the free world—soft pillows and wine and open spaces. I couldn't decide whether I wanted to drive through the mountains or go to the ocean. I could remember driving through the North Carolina mountains one spring and how incredibly free and cool and thin the air had been, and how fantastically rugged the great jags of mountainside were. There had been blooming dogwood and wood violets and pawpaws, and little icy streams that were scarcely more than a trickle and outdoor markets with corncob dolls and hooked rugs and jugs of wild honey.

There was so much to see in the world. Late at night I would pace the floor and think back over the places I had read about and seen and I would marvel that I had no ties, no commitments, nothing to hamper me from roaming the world and finding exactly what I really wanted.

On April 21 I had a card from Nell, showing two little brown field mice with the tips of their tails intertwined and under the picture she had penciled *Togetherness. You don't have to come home now or ever,* she wrote on the back, *but there was a time when we loved each other so much.*

"What am I going to *do?*" I said to Mr. Donnell. "She's fixed it so I *have* to go home, and then what do I do once I'm there?" "You don't have to go home at all," he said. "You are an adult and you have your own life and you don't have to get upset by sentimental attempts to hamper you." "But I love her," I said. "Try loving yourself for a while," he suggested. "You aren't any good to her or anyone unless you reorganize your life. What are you going to do tomorrow—I mean, what's the first step when you get out?" "I want to leave," I said, "and I keep ignoring the fact that I can't go at once because I've got to get clothes from storage and I have business matters—money matters—that will take a week. I'll go out to Jersey with Bea until I can hurry things through."

"You can't go to Jersey and you know it," Mr. Donnell said flatly. I was genuinely taken aback and I said, "Why *not?* Of course we're not going to hustle." "Because Jersey is over the state line," he said. "You know you'll most likely be followed when you leave here, and once you cross a state line with Ronald and Bea they could take you in for questioning." It had never occurred to me that when I left I would still be involved with the police. "But why?" I said. "There are at least ten other prostitutes leaving here at the same time. I know four of them who are meeting their pushers at Whalen's drug store and buying heroin. Why don't they follow them?" "I don't know," Mr. Donnell said. "For some reason you have been singled out and we both know it. Now, where are you going to stay for your week in New York?"

"I don't know," I said. "Now I'm completely confused about everything." "Well," Mr. Donnell said, "I'd suggest that you stay at a hotel in the Village, a very obscure hotel." He named several and I wrote his suggestions down, but I was in a daze. "Afterward, get out of New York," he said. "Get your business finished and leave before they get you on something else." "But what could they get me on?" I said. "I don't intend to do anything." "I don't know," Mr. Donnell said, "but please be careful and just leave as soon as possible."

Upstairs, I had a message to see Captain White and when I went down to her office she said, "I've made arrangements through Commissioner Kross for you to leave at seven A.M. There will be so many photographers and God knows who else after you that we feel you should have a head start." "Thank you," I said. "That's all right," she replied. "Just please leave New York before you have any more difficulties, and be very careful while you're here."

Almost all night I lay awake and worried; I had the frantic, helpless feeling animals must have when they're being methodically tracked down by methods far superior to their ingenuity at running and hiding. I wonder, I thought, if I'll have trouble after I leave New York. I wonder if I'll ever be *able* to leave New York. Some time during the night I got up and stood on the toilet and looked out the window. It was cool and misty and rather gray outside and I could hear foghorns from the river. I was still standing there looking out at the Village as it began to clear and become light when Dovall, a bleached-blond guard, came up and whispered: "Just put on a robe and take anything you want to keep and you can get dressed downstairs." Bea woke and said: "Call Harly when you get out and I'll meet all of you in that tavern across from the courthouse."

"I'd hurry if I were you," the guard said while I was dressing. "It's after six thirty and there may be some people out there already." "Do you honestly think anyone will be out there at this hour?" I asked her. "I don't know," she said, "but I'd be very careful. You are good for publicity and you don't want the police to trail you to wherever you're staying." She let me out a side door and I found myself on an empty street, dressed in wrinkled clothes, tired, carrying a huge stack of mail crammed into, and spilling from, seven manila envelopes. I walked around the corner and was acutely aware of high heels after almost three months in heavy oxfords. I walked down Sixth Avenue, looking for a telephone, past rows of empty stores; I balanced my spilling mail and kept looking over my shoulder to see if I were followed. After several blocks my knees began to tremble and I realized that I was not only unaccustomed to high heels, but I hadn't walked for a long time—in the weeks of lying in bed or taking an elevator (using the staircases was forbidden) my legs had all but atrophied. I felt generally weak and my clothes hung loosely from lost weight.

From a small drug store I called Harly at his home and he said: "Go back to the Howard Johnson's across from the prison and I'll meet you in a half hour."

I dialed long distance to call Nell and while I was waiting for the connection became aware of a tall, solidly built man who leaned against the magazine counter and watched me. My heart lurched and I thought, This must be someone following me. While I talked to Nell I tried to watch him from the corner of my eye and I was so distracted that Nell finally said, "What's the matter, aren't you listening to me?" "I'm listening," I said. "I just can't come home now. I love you and I want to be with you but I have to be some place where I can work and reconstruct my life." "Well, I should think so," Nell said. "After all you've had a good long rest for three months and you haven't an excuse in the world for not *doing* things now. You must get yourself groomed and see that your hair is done and have your teeth cleaned. . . ." I watched the man and he watched me. "Are you listening?" Nell said. "Or are you just thinking, I'll go my own way and wear my clothes when they're wrinkled and I'll cut my hair off and not care whether it's becoming or . . ." The man shifted his weight and took out a package of cigarettes and lighted one.

"Where are you going to stay?" Nell said. "I don't know yet," I said. "I've just been out fifteen minutes."

"Well, you've had three months to think about it," Nell said. "If you go to a hotel you be certain you know where the fire exits are, and lock your door from the inside and put on the bolt. I suppose you won't do any of these things, you'll just think you're putting something over on me when you sleep in a room with the door unlocked and don't pay any attention to where the fire exit is, but when you wake up and find . . ." The man dropped the butt of the cigarette and ground it out and resumed watching me. "I have to meet Harly," I said. "I'll call you tonight."

I gathered up my mail and walked out of the phone booth and the man walked toward me and then passed me and went into the booth. My God, I thought, the poor man was waiting for the phone and I've about had a heart attack thinking he was a detective. I plodded back down the street to the Howard Johnson's, my knees becoming weaker and weaker. My head ached from lack of sleep and I realized there had been no thrill at all in being released. I was like a canary that had escaped from its cage and had become aware it was better off in captivity. I no longer wanted champagne or a steak; I couldn't think of the future because there were too many immediate problems.

I ordered coffee and wiggled my feet partly out of my shoes and while I waited for Harly I read some of the mail that had been considered too censorable to give me but that the mail room had saved. The first letter was from an anonymous man in Albany. It went on for some five insulting pages and I skimmed after the first half page.

There was a letter from a woman in a small Texas town who said she had once stolen something and she stood up in church and confessed it in front of everybody and God forgave her, and she knew that if a woman wanted men real bad, and just couldn't stop herself from having men that God would forgive that woman if she just stood up and confessed it in front of everybody. *Maybe if you went to a doctor he could give you shots,* she added hopefully, *and make you stop wanting men so bad. That's what my cousin had to do and now she works in an office and everything is O.K.*

I was sipping coffee and reading when Harly came in and said: "My *God* you look skinny." "Thank you," I said. "Do you think I'm being followed?" "I doubt it," he replied, taking off his coat, "but if you do get picked up for questioning I'll be right down and get you out." "I've heard that song before," I said rudely. There was no particular reason to take out my misery on Harly but he was conveniently sitting there.

At the tavern where we met Bea, the press found us and for over two hours I tried to ward off questions while we were waiting for Ronald to come in from Jersey. There was one reporter who was particularly obnoxious and he started his interview by saying, "Well, Virginia, are you going back in the business?" I've forgotten exactly what I said in reply but he said indignantly, "Well, you sure as hell aren't goin' back to teaching, baby." I said, "Well, you sure as hell aren't going to pump me and get any answers so you might as well give up." I ignored him and went on talking to a nice little woman from one of the local papers who wanted to know what designer had made my poor, crumpled old black suit. "I really don't know," I said to her, "but the way it looks I doubt if any of them would claim it." "That's all right," she said. "I'll just say Hattie Carnegie; that's what we say if we're in doubt."

After Bea and Ronald left for Jersey, Harly drove me to one of the hotels Mr. Donnell had suggested and I went up to my room and lay down. I lay there from noon until seven and then I went out for dinner and saw a man standing in the corner of the lobby that I knew was a detective. I recognized him from the raid, and when he saw me coming out of the elevator he turned quickly.

On the corner I bought a copy of each paper and automatically turned to the second pages where there were candid shots of me looking tired and crumpled and disheveled. The obnoxious reporter had entitled his story HAD A BALL IN JAIL and gone on to tell about the fun I'd had being chased by, and chasing, Lesbians. I looked back toward the hotel and saw the detective walking the other way and when he turned the corner I went back upstairs, took my overnight case and left.

"Harly," I said to him over the phone, "I *am* being followed." "Well," he said, "I suppose you are, but you aren't doing anything, are you?" "That doesn't make any difference," I said. "I can't keep changing hotels and dodging them. I want Bea to go with me tomorrow and we'll get our clothes from storage and I'm leaving." "I'll see she does," Harly said, "but in the morning I want you to be at my office. There are people coming in to discuss a book and a movie about you." "Oh, my *God,*" I said, "I wouldn't have a book out about this fiasco for any price." "Just talk to them," he said. "Maybe you could write a book about prison conditions and leave yourself out. At least you can talk to them."

After dinner, which I ate between reading the newspaper stories and craning my neck to see who was behind me, I went to a women's hotel. At least they can't plant a man in my room here, I thought, trying to anticipate just what the police might do. While I was signing the register I glanced in the mirror behind the desk and saw two men who could only have been detectives, standing just outside the revolving door, watching me. I added a false address under the alias I had written and tried to make a decision. If I walked out I'd of course have them following me to wherever I went. If I went ahead upstairs it seemed possible that they would be afraid to follow unless they actually had a warrant to back themselves up. I got my key and took the elevator up to the third floor and walked back downstairs and when I came to the lobby level I stood and watched them through the glass door. They were talking to the desk clerk and there was apparently no way I could leave without walking behind them.

I went back to the first floor and rang for the elevator and when the colored operator appeared I handed him a ten-dollar bill and said, "I want you to find out what the detectives are talking to the desk clerk about." "I *know* what they're talking about," he said, "because they asked me first what room I took you to." "Is there any other way out?" I asked. He hesitated and I gave him another ten dollars. "Come on," he said. I followed him around to the other side of the first floor and down a back staircase. "You'll have to climb over the banisters," he explained. "That there gate's locked so's people can't get out this way when they ain't paid rent, and there's a burglar alarm on it." He climbed over first and lowered himself to the ground level. It was about a seven-foot drop and I was wearing very high heels. "Take your shoes off," he said. "A girl last week couldn't pay her rent, an' I got her and all her bags too out this way." I took off my shoes and handed them and my purse and bag to him and hitched up my skirt and climbed over. "See?" he said. "It was easy."

He walked ahead of me through the basement and let me out into an alley. It was very narrow and completely dark and as I made my way toward the lighted street I brushed against a pile of crates and heard a frightened howl from an alley cat that I had jostled. "Relax, toots, I'm one of you," I said and kept on going.

I took a cab until I came to a small tavern at least two miles away and then I got out and called Harly back. "You've lost them now," he said. "Just go to another hotel and get some sleep and I'll see you at nine thirty." "All right," I

said. "Can you get your hair done before then?" he added.
"I'll try," I said.

I took another cab, this time to a hotel far uptown, and
took a room and sat down on the edge of the bed and shook.
My arm was numb from carrying the heavy case and my
ankles trembled and I found myself listening intently for
footsteps outside the door. I should just leave tonight, I
thought, but what if it's the FBI following me about the
stock-swindle investigation? Then I'd just be shadowed all
over San Francisco.

I called Nell and said, "I'm sorry I couldn't talk before
but I was in a hurry." "Well," she said, "I suppose you're out
drinking. The papers here said you went right to a tavern."
I was too tired to explain. "Yes," I said, "but I'm in my hotel
now." I heard footsteps in the hall and my heart pounded.
How the hell will I get her off the phone so I can listen? I
thought. "Now Ginny," Nell said, "I want you to *get going*.
You've wasted enough time. There's no reason for you to
just wander around New York without any purpose. For your
own morale I want you to get a job, and . . ." The footsteps
went past my door but I couldn't tell where they stopped.
"You must get yourself groomed," Nell said. "I don't mean
have your hair all cut off but you can have it shaped." "I
will," I said distractedly. "I will. I'll have it cut." "I didn't
say to have it cut!" Nell said. "You *need* hair. You've got
crooked teeth and you're tall and you *need* hair. But I'm not
going to argue with you about it. You're twenty-six years old
and you've run your own life and you've made a fine mess.
I'm not going to argue. Do have your hair cut. Have your
head shaved. It doesn't make any difference *now*." She began
to cry. The footsteps started back and the elevator stopped
again. "I'll call you tomorrow," I said.

I took off my shoes and put a couple of pillows behind my
back and lay there, listening to slight noises in the hall and

my own heartbeat. I'll be damned if I'll take my clothes off, I thought. If they force that door I'll at least be dressed. I wonder if I could be getting paranoid, I thought just before I fell asleep.

"My *God* you're rude to people," Harly said the next day after I had talked to three different men about an autobiography. "What did you expect me to say to them?" I said. "That first one wanted to write my book for me and when I told him I wanted to write it myself he said, 'Well, it's a matter of whether you want to make money or play around.' What would *you* have said to him?" "I doubt that I'd have told him to go to hell," Harly said. "You know, you've changed. Since I first met you, I mean." "I *hope* I've changed," I said. "If I have to live by the laws of the jungle I hope I'm not the same idealistic fool I was. I'd be squished."

"Well, I hope this doesn't 'squish' you," Harly said, "but you can't leave New York right now." "I can't?" I said. "The attorney general's office wants to see you and Bea about the men you know who are involved in stocks, and then the FBI wants to see Bea and perhaps you. You'll have to stick around for a while." "What will I *do?*" I said. "I'm afraid to see any of my Johns and I can't just sit in a hotel." "Well," Harly said, "here are the names of some other people who called you. Call them back and maybe you can get the kind of book you want started."

After I left Harly's office I walked until I came to a little side street that had bookstalls and I spent most of the day browsing. I'll bet whoever's tailing me gets bored, I thought. I kept finding passages like *O Western Wind when wilt thou blow/ That the small rain down can rain. /Ah, Christ that my love were in my arms/ And I in my bed again,* and I found myself getting into a morbid state of mind. I bought a few books and I went to Bloomingdale's and I had a late lunch and a couple of cocktails—anything to avoid going back to the hotel. When utter weariness forced me to go back I took a hot bath and then I called the phone numbers Harly had given me. Jack O'Grady from the *Post* wanted me to meet him to discuss an article and a book, an independent film director wanted me to make a religious short on the downfall and redemption of a prostitute, and an enterprising young man had written a story to which I was to merely sign my name, telling "other young girls" how to avoid the lures of money and excitement in a big city. "I wrote it just like you were sayin' it yourself," he explained. "I had you gettin' off a bus, broke, coming into New York, and then you meet a guy and he offers you a hundred dollars. You have such a good time that you start hanging around bars, and . . ." "Is that really the way you think it happened?" I interrupted him. "Well, hell," he said, "it makes a good story, and at the end you say you're gonna marry a nice man, if one'll still have you, and you think you can have a nice house an' kids and forget all about what you did." "You sign your name on that story," I said. "I don't want mine on it." "Listen," he said, "you're getting pretty choosy about your name all of a sudden. I could get you five hundred dollars for this and . . ." "I make that much in an evening," I said. "And I don't have to use my real name."

I told the film producer that I wasn't certain I was redeemed as yet but if I decided to reform, or make short films, I'd call him. I made an appointment with Jack O'Grady for dinner that evening; several times during the afternoon I changed my mind. As I lay in bed and read poetry from the little books I'd bought the desire to write exposés and reform the world began to fade. What the hell has the world done for me? I thought. Why should I try to improve it when all I want is to escape and be alone and have some peace? When I read Gerard Manley Hopkins' "Heaven-Haven," I unconsciously marked the part about

I have desired to go
Where springs not fail
To fields where flies no sharp and sided hail
And a few lilies blow.

And I have asked to be
Where no storms come
Where the green swell is in the haven dumb
And out of the swing of the sea.

I won't go see O'Grady, I decided. If I'm going to write, it won't be about myself. I read for a while and began to feel a terrible loneliness. After the constant noise of five hundred women, and the constant presence of Bea in a tiny cell, I felt the size of the room and the resounding stillness of the hotel. At six thirty I decided to go and have dinner but refuse to do the book.

"They'll let you write the article on a sociological basis," Jack told me. "It may be an exposé magazine but they'll let you write what you want." "All right," I said finally. "I have to stay in New York for several weeks anyway, but God only knows where I'll stay. I can't stand a hotel that long, and I don't want to sign a lease." "I have a friend," Jack said, "who is an actress and she's going away to summer stock; you can take her apartment for a couple of weeks."

As I moved my things over to his friend's apartment I thought, Here I go again. For three months I sat in a jail cell and swore to myself that when I got out I'd leave this city, and stop leading a life that I detest, and here I go again.

Jack's friend turned out to be a rather pretty young ingenue with a nervous, chattering disposition, who wasn't going to stock as soon as Jack had promised but was glad to have someone to help with the rent. The first evening in her apartment I wandered around, feeling as out of place as a fish washed ashore, and she followed me and chattered while her little poodle ran underfoot. I finally sat down and tried to make myself inconspicuous with a book. "Some coffee?" she said. "Would you rather have tea?" "No thank you," I said. Oh my *God,* I thought, how painful it is to be among strangers. How painful it is to be alone in the world but how much more painful to be with people one doesn't know or love. "If it's too warm in here," she said politely, "I can open a window." "I'll open it," I said and got up and she got up and we almost collided. We murmured apologies and she opened the window and I pretended I was reading. Where do I go now? I thought. When I'm through with the article and the Attorney General, then where do I go? "I'm going to open a Coke," she said. "May I get you one?" "No thank you," I said. "If the dog bothers you, tell her to get down," she added. "Oh, I like dogs," I said.

I tried to read and it occurred to me that I would never be able to teach again. It also occurred to me that her dog didn't smell merely doggy, the poor thing stank. "Get down," I whispered, giving her a slight push. The dog snuggled up under my chin and licked as close to my mouth as she could get while I twisted the other way. "Get down," I whispered again and this time my roommate looked up and said, "Is the dog bothering you?" "Oh, I like dogs," I said. "She *loves* you," she said. "She just loves everybody." "That's nice," I said. How promiscuous, I thought. I wouldn't *have* a dog that just loved *everybody.*

At ten thirty she asked if I were ready for bed and I said only if *she* were ready for bed, and we parried around with elaborate courtesy and finally pulled out the couch. Dog climbed over to my side and curled up on my pillow. "Oh, she's so affectionate," Roommate said. We turned out the lights and lay in the dark. I had to blow my nose and I couldn't imagine what sort of polite protocol might be required if I had to climb over her, turn on the light and get a Kleenex. On the other hand it seemed impolite to sniffle. I lay there and thought about blowing my nose and my thoughts finally turned to all my other problems. I tried, I thought, to be a good teacher and here I lie in a strange apartment with this goddam little dog licking my face, and I want to blow my nose and I can't because it isn't my house. I tried *so* hard and I haven't anything to show for it, and all my books are ruined down in that goddam basement of Nell's and I don't have any place to go and I want to blow my nose. A tear trickled down my cheek and I thought, Oh, what the hell, she's probably asleep, and sniffled. Roommate popped up with a shot-from-a-gun effect and said, "Oh, dear, I know it's too cold for you. I'll close the window." If she closes the window, I thought, and I have to lie in this stuffy room with this awful dog . . . She closed the window.

The next day I met Jack and the editors of the exposé magazine for lunch and we arranged terms for an article, and then I went on to meet another reporter about another article. This time it was the obnoxious reporter who had asked me if I was going back to prostitution. We didn't get along any better at this meeting. "I can't have that kind of story with my name on it," I said. We argued and finally I said, "I'm sorry but that's how it stands. Even though I'm a prostitute I've got an ethical code and I can't write things about a field that I know unless I can tell the truth."

"Do you mean," he said, "that you'd want to write something saying you're *glad* you were a whore and you'd recommend being a whore?" "I can't say that it was any worse than some other periods of my life," I said, "and it's like any other field—for some women it's a happier way of life than any other area open to them and for some it's hell."

"Well," he said, "I suppose you'll want to legalize prostitution." "I don't know," I said. "As far as streetwalking goes, from what I've seen that isn't usually prostitution, it's a come-on for robbery or at least it's a con game. If you mean do I think a woman and a man should be legally allowed to go to bed together, in private, and with any exchange of gift

they mutually consent to, I'd say that should be legalized."
"You'd have a fine city," he said sarcastically.

"Have you ever been with a prostitute?" I asked him. "Hell yes," he said. "When I can't get it free I'll pay for it." "Well," I said, "maybe you can write an article on hypocrisy."

At eleven o'clock that night he called and said, "Look. Have you changed your mind about writing that article with me?" "No, I haven't," I said. "Well then," he said, "how about going to bed?" "I'm sorry," I said, "because I can't think of anyone I'd rather sleep with, but business is closed for the summer." "I'm not kidding you," he said. "I gotta friend with me and we just want . . ." "I'm sorry," I said and hung up.

Almost immediately the phone rang again and he said, "I'm coming up anyway." "You don't know where I live," I said and before I could hang up again he said, "Oh, yes I do." I hung up and within fifteen minutes the doorbell rang.

"We just won't answer it," I said to Roommate. It rang again and then I could hear him pounding on one of the first-floor apartments. "Hey, lemme in," he said. "I know you're in there." The pounding went on for some time and then I watched him go down the street, staggering and leaning on his friend's arm. In a couple of minutes the phone rang and he said, "I got a buddy with me that's on the Vice Squad, and you'd better let us in. He can get you busted if you don't." "If you come back again," I said, "I'll call the night editor of your paper."

In five minutes he was back downstairs, pounding on the same door, and the woman on the second floor opened her door and yelled something about the police. I watched out the window and saw the pair winding down the street, and a squad car pulled up and two uniformed police got out. While the police were talking to the neighbors the phone rang and he said, "Look you goddam whore, when my buddy an' I want . . ." I left the phone off the hook and piled throw pillows over it.

Again I lay in bed and worried and this time I tried to decide just what sort of life I could lead, from that point on. God knows, I thought, that I don't want to be a prostitute. I don't want to be a prostitute and I don't want to do somebody's office work or housework. I can and will do any of these things if necessary for some higher goal, but I don't have any higher goal now and anyway I think I can contribute more to the world than that, and if I can't contribute to the world at least I should get some pleasure from life and I can't find it in a city. I listened to the bells on the hour and half-hour and quarter-hour and at three I was still awake. I'm being literally hunted, I thought. I'm prey to the press and parasites from the Vice Squad and anyone else who wants to step in. I can pay off to one to protect me from the other and then I'm just admitting I'm at their mercy.

All through May I stayed in New York and waited through postponements for the meeting with the Attorney General, and in June he called me in and read the names of five men and I said I knew them, and he asked if I had bought stocks from them and I said no and he said thank you. "This is why I have been here a month and a half?" I said to Harly when we were outside. "No," he said, "their goddam subpoena was the reason."

Several old friends from Chicago were living near me in the Village and although I was uncertain of their reaction I looked them up. It hadn't occurred to me that my ex-convict status could cause edgy situations until Roommate asked me how I preferred to be introduced to her friends, and implied that she would prefer to use another name for me. "You can just call me Karen in front of people," I said. "What about a last name?" she asked. "Anything handy," I said, which led to several names such as Karen Kane, which could have come directly off a Minsky's poster. To my surprise my old friends

were quite calm about the situation and I spent several evenings entertaining them and all their friends by answering
questions on jail, Lesbians, Lesbians in jail, whores, whorehouses, how much you make and so on, until I longed for
the subtle prison society that veiled their curiosity under
such guises as Truth or Consequences.

After one of these question-and-answer sessions I was invited to go along for a Fourth of July excursion to Long
Beach, to swim and spend the weekend at a hotel. "Is it quiet
there?" I asked. I had seen pictures of New York-area beaches.
"We were there in May," I was told, "and it was almost deserted." I packed my bags and went and discovered that beach
conditions in May and on the Fourth of July are, so to speak,
horses of opposite shades. The beach was packed with a
blanket-to-blanket crowd and in between the blankets tod-
dlers staggered about with their pants falling off and teen-
age boys threw hard balls with great force and grade-school
boys chased each other spurting mouthfuls of water. It was
ungodly hot. I lay on the blanket and thought about the
cottage and the long, quiet, deserted beach and the cold, calm
lake. A child from the blanket next to us came over and
stuck my bottle of suntan oil in her mouth and her grandmother took a bite of banana and said, "Don't swallow nothing, Mickie," and returned to her gin rummy game.

By nine in the evening my sunburn was uncomfortable and
I went to bed. In less than an hour an explosion brought me
to an upright position. "Fireworks display," one of my friends
said. They were gathered around the windows watching.
"Oh," I said, lying back. My sunburn was red and sore and
the sand in the bed grated and I went from seizures of burning to little periods of shivering chills. Out on the beach the
display went on with one major explosion after another and
smaller bangs from private parties down on the other end. I
could see showers of red, white and blue sparks and once I
saw a lopsided design that must have been intended as an

American flag. And I used to worry about dying, I thought. I used to worry because life was so short and I was afraid of disease and atom bombs and planes. One thing my kind of life does for you—it eliminates the fear of death. Long into the night I burned and froze and watched colored rockets.

I'm leaving New York, I wrote to Nell, *as soon as I have arranged a book contract.* I got an immediate reply and she said:

If you must write a book please do not admit anything and *do not include yourself.* If you do write about yourself you can simply delete the part about prostitution—in fact, don't admit you know anything about it as a field. If you must discuss your family keep in mind that we are well-educated people, nice, were good to you when you were a child and so forth. You could relate little funny incidents *without actually telling anything on us.*

The next morning at five thirty we were awakened by a special-delivery letter in which she said:

We have had enough disgrace and there is no reason for you to add a vulgar book to the rest of it. After all you are an educated woman and can write a book that is intellectual.

I read her letter and went back to bed and at eight a delivery boy came from Mr. Kouberoff's, carrying the huge boxes of my possessions which the court had demanded him to return. When the boy left I opened the first carton and pulled out old, raggedy men's shorts, ripped and dirty cotton dresses, little rags that had once been children's sunsuits, men's rubber boots, squashed velvet hats with bits of plumes and veils still adhering. . . . I stopped and shoved the rags back in and called Kouberoff and said, "You've sent me the wrong cartons." "No I haven't," he said. "I've sent you exactly what you're going to get." I started to call Harly and then thought, No, I've fought this whole battle long enough.

There comes a time when it is better judgment to stop fighting and accept the inevitable.

The exposé magazine for which I wrote an article asked me to go to Chicago the week the issue came out, to appear on several television programs and "promote." They assigned a press agent to me and he described the way he wanted me dressed and what I was to say to columnists and so forth. At least Nell will be pleased, I thought when I was out buying clothes for the trip. Under pressure from the press agent I had discovered I could wear a size-10 dress, and it had long been Nell's contention that my clothes were too long and too loose. She *will* be pleased, I thought when I tried to sit down in the dressing room of Saks and discovered I could only perch on the edge of the chair. My hair had grown quite long in prison and I had even sprouted a few white hairs; I plucked the white hairs out and had my hair done in a full bouffant style and on a last-minute inspiration added some of my roommate's silver eyeshadow.

We arrived in Chicago at 11 A.M. and over the protests of the press agent went directly to Nell's. "Oh my *God*," Nell said promptly. *"Look* at your behind." "I can't look," I said. "My dress is so tight I can't turn around." "I don't think it's funny," Nell said. "You look like a great big peasant." "Why are you wearing your hair that way?" Nonnie said. "That looks corny." "It's long," I said, "and of course it looks corny." Before I left, Nell had me dressed in one of her new summer suits, with a suggestion that I burn what I had on. On our way downtown to the press conference I was miserable; I detested the suit and I felt foolish in it. Why didn't I tell her to mind her own business? I thought.

I talked to Nell on the telephone before I appeared on the Marty Faye show that night and she said, "Please don't make a fool of yourself." "What do you mean?" I said. "Well, try to act like a lady," Nell said. "Remember that no one admires a coarse woman." "My God," I said, "I don't think I act coarse." "Just keep Grace Kelly in mind," Nell suggested. "She always appears so well bred and so ladylike; there's something about a floozie-looking woman with too much make-up that breeds disrespect." "Are you insinuating that I look like a floozie?" I asked her. "I certainly am," Nell said. "I wasn't going to say anything over the phone but your grandmother and I were *so* embarrassed. You used to wear sports clothes so well and you had such good, classic taste and now you just look *common*. You look just plain common."

After the program she said, "Well, you did quite well but the camera must have added fifteen pounds, you looked *so* heavy. I don't like your hair that way and it made you look kind of *simple* but we thought you did very well."

We were in Chicago for three days and on my last evening I had dinner at home. "What are you going to do now?" Nell asked. "I don't know," I said. "Are you willing to admit," Nonnie asked, "that you've made an awful mess of your life?" "I'm willing to admit I'm awfully tired," I said.

On the way back to New York I felt desperately discouraged. I'm the biggest goddam fool in the world, I thought, but I don't know what to do about *it*.

Back in my apartment I picked up that day's papers and read the *Post*'s account of Billie Holliday's death in a charity hospital. I had been following her battle with the police who tried to take her over to the House of Detention while she was dying, and I thought, I wonder if anyone will realize now that the police literally hounded her to death? When she was sick she was as afraid to enter a hospital as I would be to get near the police in any way, and she waited till it was too late and then she was right—they grabbed her.

While I was reading about her funeral plans Jack O'Grady called and said, "Did you see about Lt. Crotty?" "No," I said, "I'm reading about Billie Holliday." "Well, look next to it," he said. "They've picked Lt. Crotty up for extorting from a call-girl bar."

Lt. Crotty was the detective who had arrested me the last time, and while I read the article about him it occurred to me that the papers were making quite a unique thing of it. I wonder, I thought, if they think this is something different for the Vice Squad. Any one of us—Billie Holliday or any one in the House of Detention—could tell them all about this. They're acting as though it were an isolated case; he's just one of hundreds in a racket that's as old as the oldest profession.

After I went to bed I thought about Billie Holliday, and Lt. Crotty, and the others of us involved in the New York rat race. I suppose I could write about it, I thought. But everybody writes about it. It seems everybody on the street knows that men see prostitutes and disturbed people use narcotics and cops steal, and what could anybody tell them that's new?

The next day I didn't snap out of the depression and by evening it was so severe that I was frightened. I was alone in the apartment and I didn't want to be alone and there was no one I wanted to be with. A couple of weeks before I had gone over to Marcia's and heard what the other girls had been doing while I was away. I felt very remote from all the people involved and their situations seemed petty. I didn't want to see Marcia and I didn't want to see my Chicago friends and play their version of Twenty Questions.

It was after ten when I called Mr. Donnell and said, "If I could see you some time during the next week I'd appreciate it." "Do you mean," he asked, "that you'd like to see me tonight?" "Yes," I said gratefully, "that's exactly what I mean."

"I wish," I said, after we had a couple of drinks, "that I were dead." "Do you really wish that?" Mr. Donnell said. I thought it over. "No," I said, "I don't. I'd like to be dead for about a month, but not permanently." "I didn't think you were the suicidal type," he replied. "Oh, I know I'm not," I said. "I'm too curious. That's the only thing that's kept me going this long—curiosity." "Is that why you became a psychologist?" Mr. Donnell asked. "They say that's why we choose the field." "I'm certain of it," I said. "When I was a child I wanted to see *inside* everything. I wanted to see what was in a radio and the stuffing of a chair and I used to cut carp open with a butcher knife. I was always fascinated by a garbage pail—any time no one was looking I'd practically climb in to see what was in people's garbage." "Ever find anything interesting?" Mr. Donnell said. "I suppose so," I said, "but not often, but it never discouraged me. Optimists aren't very sensible people. If nothing good is in the garbage today it doesn't mean the Hope diamond won't be there tomorrow. Just because I'm a flop today doesn't mean that I won't eventually find my way."

I talked until after two and finally he said, "You do realize that if you became Queen of England your family would write you long letters telling you not to mess up Buckingham Palace, and send you diagrams of how awkward you looked in a crown, and asking you if you could increase your position by uniting with France?" "I realize it," I said. "But I always think eventually they'll be pleased with something I've done." "And do you realize," he went on, "that you can never please them because they can't please themselves and they don't know what they want?" "I know that," I said. "Well," he said, "then you'd better stop shooting for an impossible goal and decide what *you* want. And just what do you want?"

"I want to get out of New York," I said. "I want to stop being followed and walking a tightrope because of police. I just want to find a beach somewhere and collapse." "Do you think that would satisfy you completely?" he asked. "Of course not," I said. "I just want time to catch my breath. Then I'll start making plans."

We sat in silence for a while. "Do you remember the lines in the *Rubáiyát*," I said, "about 'Ah Love! could you and I with Him conspire, To grasp this sorry Scheme of Things entire, Would not we shatter it to bits—and then Remould it nearer to the Heart's Desire'? Isn't there a great deal we'd all want to change in this scheme of things?"

"By the way," he said as I left, "have you decided just how you want the world refashioned?" "No," I said, "but almost any change would be an improvement."

Epilogue

It wasn't till september, when schools opened, that I realized I no longer had a way of life. For most of my life I had been in school or teaching school, and for academic people a new year never begins January 1—it begins the Monday after Labor Day. Now the new school year was beginning and I was no longer a part of it—or a part of anything else.

I was surprisingly well known, but I doubted I would be welcomed in a teaching post or even in a community. I did have writing and acting offers, but they all seemed temporary. And I kept wondering, after this book is completed, then what? What fills up all those years till I'm sixty-five, or a hundred and five, or however long people are destined to hang around?

I took to reading the Help Wanted columns avidly, and discovered that jobs weren't a very good idea. I couldn't take shorthand and I didn't intend to learn; in moments of desperation I reread ads for door-to-door saleswomen, the female counterparts of the Fuller Brush men and Hoover Vacuum and life-insurance men, and in even less rational

287

hours I studied the salaries of charwomen, heavy-machinery operators, laundry shirt-pressers. I considered going back to school and switching to law and was blithely told by my own attorney that I wouldn't be accepted by the bar on moral grounds. At twenty-six I was blocked in every professional direction except writing and acting, and it was suggested that if I did summer-stock work in the vicinity of Boston I should keep my bags packed lest I be suddenly invited out of town.

It was at this point that I did what most humans are forced to do anyway. I accepted a modified life. I gave up the old fancy of people-can-do-anything and took the best of what was left to me. I chose writing. I went out in the country near a bay and took a little house with a woodburning fire-place, and I poked my fire and watched the sea gulls and tried to feel grateful that I wasn't in jail and poking a mop, but there was still an acute sense of loss. I still woke every morning with a guilty feeling because I wasn't going to school. I felt retired, and in a sense I knew that I was indeed retired. I would never again be part of any particular group or community or way of life. I was dependent on my own company and resources. For all practical purposes I had no family— to them I had become a phenomenon. I was the cross they had to bear and while they seemed to enjoy it, I didn't, and I avoided them. I had one thing left—myself. After all the fanfare it had ended as do most things—not with a bang, but a whimper.

As to what I've been through and what it all meant, I'm still probably too close to it to know. I certainly wouldn't want to go through it all again. I still have an odd sense of surprise as I look back on it. But with the exception of a few white hairs, I have a nice, wholesome look that suggests a peaceful existence. I enjoy writing, and I have confidence I can earn enough as a writer to eat regularly while I am learning my craft—and not every writer has had the same post-graduate course in human nature.